**BRITISH RAIL**

# LOCO

CW00408547

## FORTY-SIXTH EDITION
## 2004

The Complete Guide to all
Locomotives which operate on
National Rail and Eurotunnel

Peter Fox & Robert Pritchard

UPDATED TO 2005 EDITION 1.1.05

ISBN 1 902336 32 1

Pocket

# CONTENTS

# PROVISION OF INFORMATION

This book has been compiled with care to be as accurate as possible, but in some cases official information is not available and the publisher cannot be held responsible for any errors or omissions. We would like to thank the companies and individuals which have been co-operative in supplying information to us. The authors of this series of books will be pleased to receive notification from readers of any inaccuracies readers may find in the series, and notification of any additional information to supplement our records and thus enhance future editions is always welcome. Please send comments to:

Robert Pritchard, Platform 5 Publishing Ltd., Wyvern House, Sark Road, Sheffield, S2 4HG, England.
**Tel:** 0114 255 2625 **Fax:** 0114 255 2471
**e-mail:** robert@platform5.com

Both the author and the staff of Platform 5 regret they are unable to answer specific queries regarding locomotives and rolling stock.

This book is updated to 17 November 2003.

# UPDATES

An update to all the books in the *British Railways Pocket Book* series is published every month in the Platform 5 magazine, **entrain**, which contains news and rolling stock information on the railways of Britain and Ireland. For further details of **entrain**, please see the advertisement on the back cover of this book.

# BRITAIN'S RAILWAY SYSTEM

## INFRASTRUCTURE & OPERATION

Britain's national railway infrastructure is now owned by a "not for dividend" company, Network Rail, following the demise of Railtrack. Many stations and maintenance depots are leased to and operated by Train Operating Companies (TOCs), but some larger stations remain under Network Rail control. The only exception is the infrastructure on the Isle of Wight, which is nationally owned and is leased to the Island Line franchisee.

Trains are operated by TOCs over Network Rail, regulated by access agreements between the parties involved. In general, TOCs are responsible for the provision and maintenance of the locomotives, rolling stock and staff necessary for the direct operation of services, whilst Network Rail is responsible for the provision and maintenance of the infrastructure and also for staff needed to regulate the operation of services.

## DOMESTIC PASSENGER TRAIN OPERATORS

The large majority of passenger trains are operated by the TOCs on fixed term franchises. Franchise expiry dates are shown in parentheses in the list of franchisees below:

| Franchise | Franchisee | Trading Name |
|---|---|---|
| Anglia Railways[2] | GB Railways plc. (until 4 April 2004) | Anglia Railways |
| Central Trains | National Express Group plc (until 1 April 2006) | Central Trains |
| Chiltern Railways | M40 Trains Ltd. (until December 2021) | Chiltern Railways |
| Cross-Country[1] | Virgin Rail Group Ltd. (until March 2012) | Virgin Trains |
| Gatwick Express | National Express Group plc (until 27 April 2011) | Gatwick Express |
| Great Eastern Railway[2] | First Group plc (until 4 April 2004) | First Great Eastern |
| Great Western Trains | First Group plc (until 3 February 2006) | First Great Western |
| InterCity East Coast | GNER Holdings Ltd. (until 4 April 2005) | Great North Eastern Railway |
| InterCity West Coast[1] | Virgin Rail Group Ltd. (until 8 March 2012) | Virgin Trains |
| Island Line | Stagecoach Holdings plc (until February 2007) | Island Line |
| LTS Rail | National Express Group plc (until 25 May 2011) | c2c |
| Merseyrail Electrics[3] | Serco/NedRail (until 20 July 2028) | Merseyrail Electrics |

| | | |
|---|---|---|
| Midland Main Line | National Express Group plc (until 27 April 2008) | Midland Mainline |
| North London Railways | National Express Group plc (until 1 September 2006) | Silverlink Train Services |
| North West Regional Railways[4] | First Group plc (until 1 April 2004) | First North Western |
| Regional Railways North East[4] | Arriva Trains Ltd | Arriva Trains Northern |
| ScotRail | National Express Group plc (until 30 September 2004) | ScotRail |
| South Central | GoVia Ltd. (Go-Ahead/Keolis). (until May 2010) | South Central |
| South Eastern[5] | | South Eastern Trains |
| South West | Stagecoach Holdings plc (until 3 February 2007) | South West Trains |
| Thames[6] | Go-Ahead Group (until 31 March 2004) | Thames Trains |
| Thameslink | GoVia Ltd. (until 1 April 2006) | Thameslink Rail |
| Wales & Borders[7] | National Express Group plc (until 6 December 2003) | Wales & Borders Trains |
| Wessex Trains | National Express Group plc (until 30 April 2006) | Wessex Trains |
| West Anglia Great Northern[8] | National Express Group plc (until 4 April 2004) | WAGN |

**Notes**:

[1] Franchise to be renegotiated by April 2004.

[2] Due to transfer to new Greater Anglia franchise, expected to be formed in April 2004.

[3] Now under control of Merseyrail PTE instead of the Strategic Rail Authority (SRA). Franchise due to be reviewed after seven years and then every five years to fit in with Merseyside Local Transport Plan.

[4] Urban and rural services currently run by Arriva Trains Northern and First North Western are due to transfer to the new Northern franchise in late 2004. Trans-Pennine services run by these operators will be taken over by the new Trans-Pennine Express franchise on 1 February 2004.

[5] New interim management company known as South Eastern Trains (SET) formed on 9 November 2003, pending award of new Integrated Kent franchise expected in early 2005. SET is a subsidiary of the SRA.

[6] Due to transfer to First Group on 1 April 2004 for two years.

[7] Arriva Trains Ltd due to take over from National Express Group on 7 December 2003 for 15 years.

[8] West Anglia half of WAGN due to transfer to new Greater Anglia franchise. A number of options are being considered for Great Northern services, including transfer to another franchise.

A major reorganisation of franchises is under way. See **entrain** for developments.

The following operators run non-franchised services only:

| Operator | Trading Name | Route |
|---|---|---|
| British Airports Authority | Heathrow Express | London Paddington–Heathrow Airport |
| Hull Trains | Hull Trains | London King's Cross–Hull |
| West Coast Railway Co. | West Coast Railway | Fort William–Mallaig* |
| | | York–Scarborough* |

* Special summer-dated services only.

# INTERNATIONAL PASSENGER OPERATIONS

Eurostar (UK) operates international passenger-only services between the United Kingdom and continental Europe, jointly with French National Railways (SNCF) and Belgian National Railways (SNCB/NMBS). Eurostar (UK) is a subsidiary of London & Continental Railways, which is jointly owned by National Express Group plc and British Airways.

In addition, a service for the conveyance of accompanied road vehicles through the Channel Tunnel is provided by the tunnel operating company, Eurotunnel.

# FREIGHT TRAIN OPERATIONS

The following operators operate freight train services under 'Open Access' arrangements:

English Welsh & Scottish Railway Ltd (EWS).
Freightliner Ltd.
GB Railfreight Ltd. (now owned by First Group)
Direct Rail Services Ltd.

# INTRODUCTION

## SCOPE

This section contains details of all locomotives which can run on Britain's national railway network, plus those of Eurotunnel. Locomotives which are owned by EWS and Freightliner which have been withdrawn from service and awaiting disposal are now listed in the main list, as are those owned by companies such as Fragonset, Harry Needle and DRS which are awaiting possible restoration to service. Only preserved locomotives which are currently used or are likely to be used on the national network in the foreseeable future are included. Others, which may be Network Rail registered but not at present certified for use, are not included, but will be found in the Platform 5 book, "Preserved locomotives and Multiple Units".

## LOCO CLASSES

Loco classes are listed in numerical order of class. Principal details and dimensions are quoted for each class in metric and/or imperial units as considered appropriate bearing in mind common UK usage. Abbreviations used are shown in Section 4.5.

All dimensions and weights are quoted for locomotives in an 'as new' condition with all necessary supplies (e.g. oil, water and sand) on board. Dimensions are quoted in the order length x width. Lengths quoted are over buffers or couplers as appropriate. All widths quoted are maxima. Where two different wheel diameter dimensions are shown, the first refers to powered wheels and the second refers to non-powered wheels.

## NUMERICAL LISTINGS

Locomotives are listed in numerical order. Where numbers actually carried are different from those officially allocated, these are noted in class headings where appropriate. Where locomotives have been recently renumbered, the most immediate previous number is shown in parentheses. Each locomotive entry is laid out as in one of the following examples:

*RSL No.  Detail  Livery  Owner  Pool*        *Allocn.  Name*

90004 b    **V**    P      IWCA          WN      City of Glasgow

In some cases where few members of a class are named, names are appended as a separate list at the end of the class listings to save space.

**Detail Differences.** Only detail differences which currently affect the areas and types of train which locomotives may work are shown. All other detail differences are specifically excluded. Where such differences occur within a class or part class, they are shown in the 'Detail' column alongside the individual locomotive number.
Standard abbreviations used are:

a         Train air brake equipment only.
b         Drophead buckeye couplers.

| | |
|---|---|
| c | Scharfenberg couplers. |
| d | Fitted with retractable Dellner couplers (for coupling to Pendolinos). |
| k | Fitted with Swinghead Automatic "buckeye" combination couplers. |
| p | Train air, vacuum and electro-pneumatic brakes. |
| r | RETB fitted |
| s | Slow Speed Control equipment. |
| v | Train vacuum brake only. |
| x | Train air and vacuum brakes ('Dual brakes'). |
| + | Additional fuel tank capacity. |
| § | Sandite laying equipment. |

In all cases use of the above abbreviations indicates the equipment indicated is normally operable. Meaning of non-standard abbreviations and symbols is detailed in individual class headings.

**Note: Where a locomotive pool code indicates a detail difference, e.g. as in WBBM which is a special pool for RETB fitted locos, then the fitting is not shown separately.**

**Codes.** Codes are used to denote the livery, owner, pool and depot of each locomotive. Details of these will be found in section 6 of this book. Where a unit or spare car is off-lease, the operation column will be left blank.

**Names.** Only names carried with official sanction are listed. As far as possible names are shown in UPPER/lower case characters as actually shown on the name carried on the vehicle(s).

# GENERAL INFORMATION

## CLASSIFICATION AND NUMBERING

All locomotives are classified and allocated numbers by the Rolling Stock Library under the TOPS numbering system, introduced in 1972. This comprises a two-digit class number followed by a three-digit serial number. Where the actual number carried by a locomotive differs from the allocated number, or where an additional number is carried to the allocated number, this is shown by a note in the class heading.

For diesel locomotives, class numbers offer an indication of engine horsepower as shown in the table below.

| Class No. Range | Engine h.p. |
|---|---|
| 01–14 | 0–799 |
| 15–20 | 800–1000 |
| 21–31 | 1001–1499 |
| 32–39 | 1500–1999 |
| 40–54, 57 | 2000–2999 |
| 55–56, 58–69 | 3000+ |

For electric locomotives class numbers are allocated in ascending numerical order under the following scheme:

Class 70–80        direct current and DC/diesel dual system locomotives.
Class 81 onwards   alternating current and AC/DC dual system locos.

Numbers in the 89xxx series (except 89001) are allocated by the Rolling Stock Library to locomotives which have been de-registered but subsequently re-registered for use on the Netwrk Rail network and whose original number has already been re-used. 89xxx numbers are normally only carried inside locomotive cabs and are not carried externally in normal circumstances.

## WHEEL ARRANGEMENT

For main line locomotives the number of driven axles on a bogie or frame is denoted by a letter (A = 1, B = 2, C = 3 etc.) and the number of non-powered axles is denoted by a number. The use of the letter 'o' after a letter indicates each axle is individually powered, whilst the '+' symbol indicates bogies are inter-coupled.

For shunting locomotives, the Whyte notation is used. In this notation the number of leading wheels are given, followed by the number of driving wheels and then the trailing wheels.

# HAULAGE CAPABILITY OF DIESEL LOCOMOTIVES

The haulage capability of a diesel locomotive depends upon three basic factors:

1. Adhesive weight. The greater the weight on the driving wheels, the greater the adhesion and more tractive power can be applied before wheelslip occurs.

2. The characteristics of its transmission. To start a train the locomotive has to exert a pull at standstill. A direct drive diesel engine cannot do this, hence the need for transmission. This may be mechanical, hydraulic or electric. The present British Standard for locomotives is electric transmission. Here the diesel engine drives a generator or alternator and the current produced is fed to the traction motors. The force produced by each driven wheel depends on the current in its traction motor. In other words, the larger the current, the harder it pulls. As the locomotive speed increases, the current in the traction motor falls, hence the *Maximum Tractive Effort* is the maximum force at its wheels the locomotive can exert at a standstill. The electrical equipment cannot take such high currents for long without overheating. Hence the *Continuous Tractive Effort* is quoted which represents the current which the equipment can take continuously.

3. The power of its engine. Not all power reaches the rail, as electrical machines are approximately 90% efficient. As the electrical energy passes through two such machines (the generator or alternator and the traction motors), the *Power at Rail* is approximately 81% (90% of 90%) of the engine power, less a further amount used for auxiliary equipment such as radiator fans, traction motor blowers, air compressors, battery charging, cab heating, Electric Train Supply (ETS) etc. The power of the locomotive is proportional to the tractive effort times the speed. Hence when on full power there is a speed corresponding to the continuous tractive effort.

# HAULAGE CAPABILITY OF ELECTRIC LOCOMOTIVES

Unlike a diesel locomotive, an electric locomotive does not develop its power on board and its performance is determined only by two factors, namely its weight and the characteristics of its electrical equipment. Whereas a diesel locomotive tends to be a constant power machine, the power of an electric locomotive varies considerably. Up to a certain speed it can produce virtually a constant tractive effort. Hence power rises with speed according to the formula given in section three above, until a maximum speed is reached at which tractive effort falls, such that the power also falls. Hence the power at the speed corresponding to the maximum tractive effort is lower than the maximum speed.

# BRAKE FORCE

The brake force is a measure of the braking power of a locomotive. This is shown on the locomotive data panels so operating staff can ensure sufficient brake power is available on freight trains.

## ELECTRIC TRAIN SUPPLY (ETS)

A number of locomotives are equipped to provide a supply of electricity to the train being hauled to power auxiliaries such as heating, cooling fans, air conditioning and kitchen equipment. ETS is provided from the locomotive by means of a separate alternator (except Class 33 locos, which have a DC generator). The ETS index of a locomotive is a measure of the electrical power available for train supply.

Similarly, most loco-hauled coaches also have an ETS index, which in this case is a measure of the power required to operate equipment mounted in the coach. The sum of the ETS indices of all the hauled vehicles in a train must not exceed the ETS index of the locomotive.

ETS is commonly (but incorrectly) known as ETH (Electric Train Heating), which is a throwback to the days before loco-hauled coaches were equipped with electrically powered auxiliary equipment other than for train heating.

## ROUTE AVAILABILITY (RA)

This is a measure of a railway vehicle's axle load. The higher the axle load of a vehicle, the higher the RA number on a scale from 1 to 10. Each Network Rail route has a RA number and in general no vehicle with a higher RA number may travel on that route without special clearance.

## MULTIPLE & PUSH-PULL WORKING

Multiple working between vehicles (i.e. two or more powered vehicles being driven from one cab) is facilitated by jumper cables connecting the vehicles. However, not all types are compatible with each other, and a number of different systems are in use, each system being incompatible with any other.

**Association of American Railroads (AAR) System:** Classes 59, 66, and 67.
**Blue Star Coupling Code:** Classes 20, 25, 31, 33, & 37.
**Green Circle Coupling Code:** Class 47 (not all equipped).
**Orange Square Coupling Code:** Class 50.
**Red Diamond Coupling Code:** Classes 56 and 58.
**SR System:** Classes 33/1, 73 and various electric multiple units.
**Within Own Class only:** Classes 43 and 60.

Many locomotives use a time-division multiplex (TDM) system for push-pull and multiple working which utilises the existing RCH jumper cables fitted to coaching stock vehicles. Previously these cables had only been used to control train lighting and public address systems.

Class 47 locos 47701–47717 were equipped with a older non-standard TDM system.

# 1. DIESEL LOCOMOTIVES

**Note:** The 01/5 series has been allocated for shunting locomotives of various types which may operate on the Network Rail system. Only those actually registered on TOPS, or ex-BR locos are included here.

## SERIES 01/5          H-B/CATERPILLAR          0-6-0

**Built:** 1971 by The Hunslet Engine Company at Leeds (Works No. 7018), for the National Coal Board, Western Area (No. 8D). Subsequently sold to Hunslet-Barclay, Kilmarnock and rebuilt prior to sale to The Felixstowe Dock and Railway Company in 1999. Registered for use on the Railtrack network in 1999. Normally used at Felixstowe South Container Terminal.
**Engine:** Caterpillar 3412C DITA of 475 kW (640 h.p.) at ? r.p.m.
**Transmission:** Hydraulic. Twin Disc 13800 series torque converter coupled to a Hunslet final drive.
**Maximum Tractive Effort:** 180 kN (40365 lbf).
**Train Brakes:** Air.

| | |
|---|---|
| **Brake Force:** 48 t. | **Dimensions:** 3.95 x 2.51 m. |
| **Weight:** 64.3 t. | **Wheel Diameter:** 1143 mm. |
| **Design Speed:** 15 m.p.h. | **Maximum Speed:** 15 m.p.h. |
| **Fuel Capacity:** 930 litres. | **RA:** 7. |
| **Train Supply:** Not equipped. | **Multiple Working:** Not equipped. |

**Non standard numbering:** Also carries number H4323.

01531    **FX**   FX   MBDL      FX      COLONEL TOMLINE

## SERIES 01/5       ENGLISH ELECTRIC/RR        0-4-0

**Built:** 1966 by English Electric at Vulcan Foundry, Newton le Willows (Works No. D1122), for the Central Electricity Generating Board at Croydon 'B' Power Station (No. 2). Subsequently acquired by RFS(E), Doncaster (now Wabtec).
**Engine:** ? of 235 kW (315 h.p.) at ? r.p.m.
**Transmission:** Hydraulic.
**Maximum Tractive Effort:**
**Train Brakes:** Air.

| | |
|---|---|
| **Brake Force:** 10 t. | **Dimensions:** 7.32 x ? m. |
| **Weight:** 24.0 t. | **Wheel Diameter:** |
| **Design Speed:** 10 m.p.h. | **Maximum Speed:** 10 m.p.h. |
| **Fuel Capacity:** 1365 litres. | **RA:** 0. |
| **Train Supply:** Not equipped. | **Multiple Working:** Not equipped. |

**Non standard livery:** RFS(E) livery of blue, lined out in silver.

01551    **0**    WA   MBDL      ZB

## SERIES 01/5        HNRC/ROLLS-ROYCE          0-6-0

**Built:** 1966 by Thomas Hill at Vanguard Works, Kilnhurst (Works No. 167V), for ICI Billingham (No. D3). Subsequently sold to Harry Needle Railroad Company in 1995 and rebuilt 2000. Registered for use on the Railtrack network in 2000, and hired to Creative Logistics, for use at Salford International Railfreight Terminal.

**Engine:** Rolls Royce 8-cylinder of 275 kW (370 h.p.) at ? r.p.m.
**Transmission:** Hydraulic. Twin Disc 11800 torque converter coupled to a RF final drive unit.
**Maximum Tractive Effort:**
**Train Brakes:** Air.

| | |
|---|---|
| **Brake Force:** 19 t. | **Dimensions:** 9.14 x ? m. |
| **Weight:** 49.0 t. | **Wheel Diameter:** |
| **Design Speed:** 10 m.p.h. | **Maximum Speed:** 10 m.p.h. |
| **Fuel Capacity:** 1360 litres. | **RA:** 5. |
| **Train Supply:** Not equipped. | **Multiple Working:** Not equipped. |

**Non standard livery:** Creative Logistics livery of blue and green.

| 01552 | **0** | HN | MBDL | BH | |

## SERIES 01/5    BR/ENGLISH ELECTRIC    0-6-0

**Built:** 1950 by BR at Derby Locomotive Works to LMS design as BR Class 12082. Withdrawn from service in 1971 and sold to Shellstar (UK), Ince (later UK Fertilisers) in 1972. Purchased by Harry Needle in 19??, and registered for use on the Railtrack network in 2000. Part of the Harry Needle hire fleet.
**Engine:** English Electric 6KT of 260 kW (350 h.p.) at 600 r.p.m.
**Main Generator:** English Electric 801.
**Traction Motors:** Two English Electric 506.
**Maximum Tractive Effort:** 156 kN (35000 lbf).
**Continuous Tractive Effort:** ? at 8.5 m.p.h.

| | |
|---|---|
| **Power at Rail:** | **Train Brakes:** Air. |
| **Brake Force:** 19 t. | **Dimensions:** 8.88 x 2.59 m. |
| **Weight:** 48.60 t. | **Wheel Diameter:** 1232 mm. |
| **Design Speed:** 20 m.p.h. | **Maximum Speed:** 20 m.p.h. |
| **Fuel Capacity:** 3000 litres. | **RA:** 5. |
| **Train Supply:** Not equipped. | **Multiple Working:** Not equipped. |

**Non-standard numbering:** Also carries original number 12082.

| 01553 (12082) | **HN** | HN | HNRL | ZB | |

## CLASS 03      BR/GARDNER      0-6-0

**Built:** 1962 by BR at Swindon Works. Used at Hornsey T&RSMD.
**Engine:** Gardner 8L3 of 152 kW (204 h.p.) at 1200 r.p.m.
**Transmission:** Mechanical. Fluidrive type 23 hydraulic coupling to Wilson-Drewry CA5R7 gearbox with SCG type RF11 final drive.
**Maximum Tractive Effort:** 68 kN (15300 lbf).
**Continuous Tractive Effort:** 68 kN (15300 lbf) at 3.75 m.p.h.
**Train Brakes:** Air & vacuum.

| | |
|---|---|
| **Brake Force:** 13 t. | **Dimensions:** 7.93 x 2.59 m. |
| **Weight:** 31.3 t. | **Wheel Diameter:** 1092 mm. |
| **Design Speed:** 28.5 m.p.h. | **Maximum Speed:** 28.5 m.p.h. |
| **Fuel Capacity:** 1364 litres. | **RA:** 1. |
| **Train Supply:** Not equipped. | **Multiple Working:** Not equipped. |

Originally numbered D 2179.

| 03179 | **WN** | WN | HQXX | HE | CLIVE |

# CLASS 07  RUSTON & HORNSBY/PAXMAN  0-6-0

**Built:** 1962 by Ruston & Hornsby, Lincoln, as BR D2985 for shunting duties in Southampton Docks. Withdrawn from service in 1977 and sold to Tilsley & Lovatt, Stoke-on-Trent in 1978. Resold to Staveley Lime Company (later Peakstone Ltd.), Peak Dale, in 1978. Purchased by Harry Needle in 1989 and registered for use on the Railtrack network in 2000. Part of the Harry Needle Railroad Company hire fleet.
**Engine:** Paxman 6RPHL Mk. 3 of 204 kW (275 h.p.) at 1360 r.p.m.
**Main Generator:** AEI RTB 6652.
**Traction Motors:** AEI RTA 6652.
**Maximum Tractive Effort:** 126 kN (28240 lbf).
**Continuous Tractive Effort:** ? at 4.4 m.p.h.

| | |
|---|---|
| **Power at Rail:** | **Train Brakes:** Air. |
| **Brake Force:** 21 t. | **Dimensions:** 8.13 x 2.57 m. |
| **Weight:** 42.25 t. | **Wheel Diameter:** 1067 mm. |
| **Design Speed:** 20 m.p.h. | **Maximum Speed:** 20 m.p.h. |
| **Fuel Capacity:** | **RA:** 6. |
| **Train Supply:** Not equipped. | **Multiple Working:** Not equipped. |

Originally numbered D 2985.

07001      **HN**   HN   HNRL           BH

# CLASS 08         BR/ENGLISH ELECTRIC        0-6-0

**Built:** 1955–1962 by BR at Crewe, Darlington, Derby Locomotive, Doncaster or Horwich Works.
**Engine:** English Electric 6KT of 298 kW (400 h.p.) at 680 r.p.m.
**Main Generator:** English Electric 801.
**Traction Motors:** Two English Electric 506.
**Maximum Tractive Effort:** 156 kN (35000 lbf).
**Continuous Tractive Effort:** 49 kN (11100 lbf) at 8.8 m.p.h.

| | |
|---|---|
| **Power At Rail:** 194 kW (260 h.p.). | **Train Brakes:** Air & vacuum. |
| **Brake Force:** 19 t. | **Dimensions:** 8.92 x 2.59 m. |
| **Weight:** 49.6–50.4 t. | **Wheel Diameter:** 1372 mm. |
| **Design Speed:** 20 m.p.h. | **Maximum Speed:** 15 m.p.h. |
| **Fuel Capacity:** 3037 litres. | **RA:** 5. |
| **Train Supply:** Not equipped. | **Multiple Working:** Not equipped. |

**Notes:** † – Equipped with remote control (Hima Sella system) for working at Allied Steel & Wire, Cardiff.
§ – Equipped with remote control (Cattron system) for evaluation purposes.

**Non-standard liveries/numbering:**

08414 As **DG**, but with BR & Railfreight Distribution logos and large bodyside numbers. Carries number D3529.
08442 Dark grey lower bodyside with light grey upper bodyside.
08460 Light grey with black underframe, cab doors, window surrounds and roof. Carries number D3575.

08527 Light grey with a black roof, blue bodyside stripe and "Ilford Level 5" branding.
08568 and 08730 Special Alstom (Springburn) livery. Dark grey lower bodyside with a light grey upper bodyside. Red solebar stripe.
08573 Light grey.
08601 London Midland & Scottish Railway style black.
08616 carries number 3783.
08629 Red with italic numbers.
08642 London & South Western Railway style black. Carries number D3809.
08649 Grey with blue, white and red stripes and Alstom logo. Carries number D3816.
08678 Glaxochem grey and blue.
08682 Dark blue with a grey roof.
08715 "Day-glo" orange.
08721 As **B**, but with a black roof and "Express parcels" branding with red and yellow stripe.
08785 Silver grey.
08801 carries number 801.
08805 London Midland & Scottish Railway style maroon. Carries number 3973.
08809 Plain light grey.
08834 RFS(E) livery of blue with silver lining.
08883 Caledonian Railway style blue.
08928 As **F0** with large bodyside numbers and light blue solebar.

Originally numbered in series D 3000–4192.

**Class 08/0. Standard Design.**

| | | | | | | | | | | |
|---|---|---|---|---|---|---|---|---|---|---|
| 08077 | | **FL** | P | DFLS | FD | 08480 | a | **E** | E | WSMD | TO |
| 08308 | a | **CS** | RT | MOLO | IS | 08481 | | **B** | E | WSXX | SP |
| 08331 | | **GN** | WA | RFSH | EC | 08482 | a | **E** | E | WSAS | OC |
| 08375 | a | **RT** | RT | MOLO | ZB | 08483 | a | **GL** | FG | HJXX | PM |
| 08389 | a | **E** | E | WSNE | IM | 08484 | a | **DG** | AM | KWSW | ZN |
| 08393 | a | **E** | E | WSNE | IM | 08485 | a | **B** | E | WSNW | AN |
| 08397 | a | **E** | E | WSNW | AN | 08489 | a | **E** | E | WSSC | ML |
| 08401 | a | **DG** | E | WSNE | IM | 08492 | a | **B** | E | WSYX | ML |
| 08402 | a | **E** | E | WSSC | ML | 08493 | a | **B** | RT | MOLO | CF |
| 08405 | a | **E** | E | WSAS | OC | 08495 | | **E** | E | WSNE | IM |
| 08410 | a | **GL** | FG | HJXX | LA | 08499 | a | **E** | E | WSGW | CF |
| 08411 | a | **B** | E | WSSC | ML | 08500 | | **E** | E | WSWX | FB |
| 08414 | a | **0** | E | WSWX | FB | 08506 | a | **B** | E | WSAS | OC |
| 08417 | a | **SB** | SO | CDJD | ZA | 08507 | a | **HN** | HN | HNRL | CZ |
| 08418 | a | **E** | E | WSMD | TO | 08509 | a | **F** | E | WSWX | IM |
| 08428 | a | **B** | E | WSNE | IM | 08510 | a | **B** | E | WSNE | IM |
| 08441 | a | **E** | E | WSSC | ML | 08511 | a | **E** | E | WSSC | ML |
| 08442 | a | **0** | E | WSAS | OC | 08512 | a | **E** | E | WSNE | IM |
| 08451 | | **GB** | VW | ATLO | WN | 08514 | a | **E** | E | WSNE | IM |
| 08454 | | **SL** | VW | ATLO | WN | 08516 | a | **E** | E | WSMD | TO |
| 08460 | a | **0** | E | WSNW | AN | 08523 | | **ML** | E | WNZX | CD |
| 08466 | a† | **E** | E | WSNE | IM | 08525 | | **F** | MA | HISL | NL |
| 08472 | a | **BR** | WA | RFSH | BN | 08526 | | **E** | E | WSAS | OC |

| | | | | |
|---|---|---|---|---|
| 08527 | 0 | BT | KCSI | ZI (S) |
| 08528 | DG | E | WSMD | TO |
| 08529 | B | E | WSWX | DR |
| 08530 | FL | P | DFLS | FD |
| 08531 a | DG | P | DFLS | FD |
| 08534 | DG | E | WSWX | ML |
| 08535 | DG | E | WNZX | CD |
| 08536 | B | MA | HISE | DY (S) |
| 08538 | DG | E | WSMD | TO |
| 08540 | E | E | WSMD | TO |
| 08541 | DG | E | WSXX | OC |
| 08542 | F | E | WSXX | BS |
| 08543 | DG | E | WSMD | TO |
| 08561 | B | E | WSNW | AN |
| 08567 | E | E | WSMD | TO |
| 08568 a | 0 | AM | KGSS | ZH |
| 08569 | E | E | WSMD | TO |
| 08571 a | B | WA | HBSH | ZB |
| 08573 | 0 | RT | KCSI | ZI |
| 08575 | FL | P | DFLS | FD |
| 08576 | B | HN | HNRS | CF |
| 08577 | E | E | WSMD | TO |
| 08578 | E | E | WSNE | IM |
| 08580 | E | E | WSMD | TO |
| 08582 a | DG | E | WSNE | IM |
| 08585 | FL | P | DFLS | FD |
| 08587 | E | E | WSNE | IM |
| 08588 | BR | MA | HISL | ZB (S) |
| 08593 | E | E | WSNW | AN |
| 08596 a† | WA | WA | RFSH | ZB |
| 08597 | E | E | WSNE | IM |
| 08599 | E | E | WSNE | IM |
| 08601 | 0 | E | WSYX | SP |
| 08605 | B | E | WSWX | FB |
| 08611 | V | VW | ATLO | LL |
| 08613 | K | RT | | ZI |
| 08616 | GW | MA | HGSS | TS |
| 08617 | VP | VW | ATLO | WN |
| 08623 | E | E | WSNE | IM |
| 08624 | FL | P | DFLS | FD |
| 08628 | B | E | WSXX | SY |
| 08629 | 0 | AM | KWSW | ZN |
| 08630 | E | E | WSGW | CF |
| 08631 | N | FG | SDFR | ZD |
| 08632 | E | E | WSNW | AN |
| 08633 | E | E | WSNE | IM |
| 08635 | B | E | WSAS | OC |
| 08641 | FP | FG | HJSL | LA |
| 08642 | 0 | P | DFLS | FD |
| 08644 | GL | FG | HJSL | LA |
| 08645 | FP | FG | HJSL | LA |
| 08646 | F | E | WSAS | OC |
| 08648 | DG | RT | MOLO | ZB (S) |
| 08649 | 0 | AM | KESE | ZG |
| 08651 a | DG | E | WSGW | CF |
| 08653 | E | E | WSMD | TO |
| 08655 | F | E | WSNE | IM |
| 08662 | E | E | WSGW | CF |
| 08663 a | GL | FG | HJSL | PM |
| 08664 | E | E | WSAS | OC |
| 08665 | E | E | WSNE | IM |
| 08666 | B | E | WNZX | SP |
| 08669 a | WA | WA | RFSH | BN |
| 08670 a | E | E | WSSC | ML |
| 08675 | F | E | WSXX | ML |
| 08676 | E | E | WSGW | CF |
| 08678 | 0 | WC | MBDL | CS |
| 08682 | 0 | BT | KDSD | ZF |
| 08683 | E | E | WSMD | TO |
| 08685 | B | E | WSGW | CF |
| 08689 a | E | E | WSNE | IM |
| 08690 | MA | MA | HISE | DY (S) |
| 08691 | FL | WA | DFLS | FD |
| 08694 a | E | E | WSAS | OC |
| 08695 a | E | E | WSSC | ML |
| 08696 a | V | VW | ATLO | LO |
| 08697 | B | MA | HISE | DY (S) |
| 08698 a | E | E | WSMD | TO |
| 08701 a | RX | E | WSNW | AN |
| 08702 | B | E | WNZX | ZB |
| 08703 a | E | E | WSMD | TO |
| 08706 | E | E | WSNW | AN |
| 08709 | E | E | WSMD | TO |
| 08711 | RX | E | WSAS | OC |
| 08714 | E | E | WSMD | TO |
| 08715 v | 0 | E | WSWX | FB |
| 08720 a | E | E | WSXX | ML |
| 08721 | 0 | VW | ATLO | LO |
| 08724 | WA | WA | HBSH | NL |
| 08730 | 0 | AM | KGSS | ZH |
| 08735 | E | E | WSNE | IM |
| 08737 a | FE | E | WSNW | AN |
| 08738 | E | E | WSNW | AN |
| 08739 | B | E | WSXX | AN |
| 08740 | F | E | WSXX | FB |
| 08742 | RX | E | WSMD | TO |
| 08743 | EN | EN | MBDL | BG |
| 08745 | FE | P | DFLS | FD |
| 08750 a | K | RT | MOLO | ZB |
| 08751 | FE | E | WNZX | ZB |
| 08752 † | E | E | WSAW | CF |
| 08754 | FL | RT | MOLO | ZB |

▲ Departmental grey-liveried 08922 is seen shunting at Carlisle Currock yard on 08/09/03.　**Robert Pritchard**

▼ EWS-liveried 09003 at Margan yard on 30/08/02.　**Rodney Lissenden**

DRS-liveried 20301 "Max Joule 1958–1999" and 20302 top-and-tail a short train of flats into Workington docks on 06/05/03. **Dave McAlone**

▲ Railtrack blue-liveried 31601 "BLETCHLEY PARK STATION X" is seen stabled at Peterborough on 15/04/03. **John Rudd**

▼ Fragonset-liveried 33021 "Eastleigh" and 33108 "VAMPIRE" lead Class 423 3529 through Eastleigh on 05/10/02. **Mervyn Turvey**

▲ EWS-liveried 37670 "St. Blazey T&RS Depot" is seen at Tyne Yard on 16/07/03 with 6D43 14.57 Jarrow–Lindsey. **Paul Shannon**

▼ BR Blue-liveried 40145 passes Frinkley Lane, near Grantham with the 17.03 London King's Cross–Crewe charter on 06/09/03. **Paul Robertson**

43007 in new Midland Mainline "Meridian" livery leads a Nottingham–London St. Pancras train south at Wellingborough on 14/05/03.

**John Rudd**

▲ A GNER-liveried HST with power cars 43115 and 43114 pass Larbert with the 07.55 Inverness–London King's Cross on 26/03/03. **Ian Lothian**

▼ The Network Rail New Measurement Train, with power cars 43014 and 43062 (nearest camera) is seen near Leighton Buzzard on 20/08/03. **Anthony Kay**

▲ Freightliner-liveried 47150 passes South Morton with 4027 05.27 Trafford Park–Southampton Freightliner on 19/08/03. **Anthony Kay**

▼ Cotswold Rail-liveried 47200 "The Fosse Way" pauses at Reading on 25/03/03 with a Cardiff–Ipswich Freightliner. **Darren Ford**

56018 passes Barnetby on 16/06/03 with an empty m.g.r. coal train.

**Paul Shannon**

| | | | | | | | | | |
|---|---|---|---|---|---|---|---|---|---|
| 08756 | | **DG** | RT | MOLO | ZB | 08867 | **K** | E | WSWX | FB |
| 08757 | | **RG** | E | WSMD | TO | 08868 | **B** | HN | HNRL | BH |
| 08758 | | **B** | E | WSYX | FB | 08869 | **G** | HN | HNRL | BH (S) |
| 08762 | | **B** | RT | MOLO | QU | 08870 | **RL** | RL | MBDL | MS |
| 08765 | | **DG** | E | WSMD | TO | 08871 | **CD** | CD | CROL | ZB |
| 08768 | | **B** | E | WSWX | ML | 08872 | **E** | E | WSAS | OC |
| 08770 | a | **DG** | E | WSGW | CF | 08873 | **RX** | RT | MOLO | CP |
| 08775 | | **E** | E | WSAS | OC | 08874 | **SL** | RT | MOLO | CP |
| 08776 | a | **DG** | E | WSAS | OC | 08877 | **DG** | E | WSWX | SP |
| 08782 | a | **CU** | E | WSNW | AN | 08879 | **E** | E | WSWX | FB |
| 08783 | | **E** | E | WSAS | OC | 08880 | **B** | E | WSXX | AN |
| 08784 | | **E** | E | WSNE | IM | 08881 | **DG** | E | WSSC | ML |
| 08785 | a | **0** | P | DFLS | FD | 08883 | **0** | E | WSSC | ML |
| 08786 | a | **DG** | E | WSAS | OC | 08884 | **B** | E | WSMD | TO |
| 08788 | | **RT** | RT | MOLO | IS | 08886 § | **E** | E | WSNE | IM |
| 08790 | | **B** | VW | ATLO | LO | 08887 | a | **VP** | VW | ATLO | LO |
| 08792 | | **F** | E | WSGW | CF | 08888 | **E** | E | WSNE | IM |
| 08795 | | **FP** | FG | HJSE | LE | 08890 | **DG** | E | WSAS | OC |
| 08798 | | **E** | E | WSWX | TO | 08891 | **B** | P | DFLS | FD |
| 08799 | a | **E** | E | WSNE | IM | 08892 | **GN** | WA | RFSH | ZB |
| 08801 | | **B** | RT | MOLO | ZB | 08893 | **DG** | E | WSYX | FB |
| 08802 | | **RX** | E | WSNW | AN | 08894 | **B** | E | WSXX | AN |
| 08804 | | **E** | E | WSAS | OC | 08896 | **E** | E | WSGW | CF |
| 08805 | | **0** | MA | HGSS | SI | 08897 | **E** | E | WSNW | AN |
| 08806 | a | **F** | E | WSXX | TE | 08899 | **MM** | MA | HISE | DY |
| 08807 | | **BR** | E | WSSC | ML | 08900 | **DG** | E | WSAS | OC |
| 08809 | | **0** | CD | CREL | MM | 08901 | **B** | E | WSYX | FB |
| 08810 | a | **AR** | CD | CREL | MM | 08902 | **B** | E | WSXX | AN |
| 08813 | a | **DG** | E | WSYX | TE | 08903 | **EN** | EN | MBDL | BG |
| 08815 | | **B** | E | WSYX | SP | 08904 | **E** | E | WSGW | CF |
| 08817 | | **BR** | E | WSYX | SP | 08905 | **E** | E | WSMD | TO |
| 08818 | | **HN** | HN | DFLS | FD | 08906 | **B** | E | WSXX | ML |
| 08819 | | **DG** | RT | MOLO | ZB | 08907 | **E** | E | WSAS | OC |
| 08822 | | **GL** | FG | HJSE | PM | 08908 | **MM** | MA | HISL | NL |
| 08823 | a | **B** | BT | KDSD | ZF | 08909 | **ML** | E | WSNW | AN |
| 08824 | ak | **F** | E | WSNE | IM | 08910 | **B** | E | WSXX | FB |
| 08825 | a | **B** | E | WSYX | SP | 08911 | **DG** | E | WSNE | IM |
| 08827 | a | **B** | E | WSYX | ML | 08912 | **B** | E | WSWX | FB |
| 08828 | a | **E** | E | WSMD | TO | 08913 | **E** | E | WSGW | CF |
| 08830 | | **LW** | WB | HLSV | CP | 08914 | **B** | E | WSYX | FB |
| 08834 | | **0** | WA | HBSH | ZB | 08915 | **F** | E | WSNW | AN |
| 08836 | | **GL** | FG | HJXX | PM | 08918 | **DG** | E | WSAS | OC |
| 08837 | | **DG** | E | WSXX | AN | 08919 | **RX** | E | WSAS | OC |
| 08842 | | **E** | E | WSNW | AN | 08920 | **F** | E | WSMD | TO |
| 08844 | | **E** | E | WSAS | OC | 08921 † | **E** | E | WSAS | OC |
| 08847 | | **CD** | CD | CREL | MM | 08922 | **DG** | E | WSNW | AN |
| 08853 | a | **B** | WA | RFSH | BN | 08924 | **E** | E | WSSC | ML |
| 08854 | † | **E** | E | WSAS | OC | 08925 | **B** | E | WSWX | DR |
| 08856 | | **B** | E | WSGW | CF | 08926 | **B** | E | WSXX | AN |
| 08865 | | **E** | E | WSGW | CF | 08927 | **B** | E | WSSC | ML |
| 08866 | | **E** | E | WSNW | AN | 08928 | **0** | HN | HNRL | BH (S) |

| 08931 | **B** | E | WSYX | FB |
|-------|-------|---|------|-----|
| 08932 | **B** | E | WSXX | CD |
| 08933 | **E** | E | WSSC | ML |
| 08934 a | **VP** | VW | ATLO | WN |
| 08936 | **HN** | HN | HNRL | BH |
| 08939 | **E** | E | WSMD | TO |
| 08941 | **E** | E | WSGW | CF |
| 08942 | **B** | E | WSXX | FB |
| 08946 | **FE** | E | WSWX | AN |

| 08947 | **B** | E | WSAS | OC |
|-------|-------|---|------|-----|
| 08948 c | **EP** | EU | GPSS | NP |
| 08950 | **IM** | MA | HISL | ZB (S) |
| 08951 † | **E** | E | WSAW | CF |
| 08953 a | **DG** | E | WSNE | IM |
| 08954 | **F** | E | WSNW | AN |
| 08955 | **F** | E | WSXX | CF |
| 08956 | **SB** | SO | CDJD | ZA |
| 08957 | **E** | HN | HNRS | CF |

**Names:**

| | |
|---|---|
| 08389 | NOEL KIRTON OBE |
| 08483 | DUSTY Driver David Miller |
| 08568 | St. Rollox |
| 08585 | Vicky |
| 08649 | G.H. Stratton |
| 08664 | DON GATES 1952–2000 |
| 08682 | Lionheart |
| 08691 | Terri |
| 08694 | PAT BARR |
| 08701 | The Sorter |
| 08714 | Cambridge |
| 08730 | The Caley |
| 08743 | Brian Turner |
| 08782 | CASTLETON WORKS |
| 08790 | M.A. SMITH |
| 08799 | ANDY BOWER |
| 08804 | RICHARD J.WENHAM EASTLEIGH DEPOT DECEMBER 1989–JULY 1999 |
| 08818 | MOLLY |
| 08844 | CHRIS WREN 1955–2002 |
| 08872 | TONY LONG Stratford Depot 1971–2002 |
| 08874 | Catherine |
| 08896 | STEPHEN DENT |
| 08903 | John W Antill |
| 08905 | Danny Daniels |
| 08919 | Steep Holm |
| 08950 | Neville Hill 1st |
| 08951 | FRED |

**Class 08/9. Reduced height cab.** Converted 1985–1987 by BR at Landore T&RSMD.

| 08993 | **E** | E | WSGW | CF | ASHBURNHAM |
|-------|-------|---|------|-----|------------|
| 08994 a | **E** | E | WSGW | CF | GWENDRAETH |
| 08995 a | **E** | E | WSGW | CF | KIDWELLY |

# CLASS 09       BR/ENGLISH ELECTRIC       0-6-0

**Built:** 1959–1962 by BR at Darlington or Horwich Works.
**Engine:** English Electric 6KT of 298 kW (400 h.p.) at 680 r.p.m.
**Main Generator:** English Electric 801.
**Traction Motors:** English Electric 506.
**Maximum Tractive Effort:** 111 kN (25000 lbf).

**Continuous Tractive Effort:** 39 kN (8800 lbf) at 11.6 m.p.h.
**Power At Rail:** 201 kW (269 h.p.).          **Train Brakes:** Air & vacuum.
**Brake Force:** 19 t.                          **Dimensions:** 8.92 x 2.59 m.
**Weight:** 50 t.                               **Wheel Diameter:** 1372 mm.
**Design Speed:** 27 m.p.h.                     **Maximum Speed:** 27 m.p.h.
**Fuel Capacity:** 3037 litres.                 **RA:** 5.
**Train Supply:** Not equipped.                 **Multiple Working:** Not equipped.

Class 09/0 were originally numbered D 3665–71, 3719–21, 4099–4114.

**Class 09/0. Built as Class 09.**

| | | | | | |
|---|---|---|---|---|---|
| 09001 | E | E | WSGW | CF | |
| 09003 | E | E | WSGW | CF | |
| 09005 | E | E | WSNE | IM | |
| 09006 | E | E | WSAS | OC | |
| 09007 | ML | E | WSNE | IM | |
| 09008 | E | E | WSGW | CF | |
| 09009 | E | E | WSAS | OC | Three Bridges C.E.D. |
| 09010 | DG | E | WSAS | OC | |
| 09011 | DG | E | WSGW | CF | |
| 09012 | DG | E | WSAS | OC | Dick Hardy |
| 09013 | DG | E | WSGW | CF | |
| 09014 | DG | E | WSNE | IM | |
| 09015 | E | E | WSGW | CF | |
| 09016 | E | E | WSGW | CF | |
| 09017 | E | E | WSGW | CF | |
| 09018 | E | E | WSAS | OC | |
| 09019 | ML | E | WSAS | OC | |
| 09020 | E | E | WSNW | AN | |
| 09021 | E | E | WSNW | AN | |
| 09022 a | E | E | WSNW | AN | |
| 09023 a | E | E | WSNE | IM | |
| 09024 | ML | E | WSAS | OC | |
| 09025 | CX | SC | HWSU | SU | |
| 09026 | G | SC | HWSU | BI | Cedric Wares |

**Class 09/1. Converted from Class 08/0. 110 V electrical equipment.**

**Converted:** 1992–93 by RFS Industries, Kilnhurst.

| | | | | | |
|---|---|---|---|---|---|
| 09101 (08833) | DG | E | WSGW | CF | |
| 09102 (08832) | DG | E | WSGW | CF | |
| 09103 (08766) | DG | E | WSSC | ML | |
| 09104 (08749) | DG | E | WSXX | AN | |
| 09105 (08835) | DG | E | WSGW | CF | |
| 09106 (08759) | DG | E | WSNE | IM | |
| 09107 (08845) | DG | E | WSNE | IM | |

**Class 09/2. Converted from Class 08. 90 V electrical equipment.**

**Converted:** 1992 by RFS Industries, Kilnhurst.

| | | | | | |
|---|---|---|---|---|---|
| 09201 (08421) | ak DG | E | WSNE | IM | |
| 09202 (08732) | DG | E | WSNE | IM | |

| 09203 | (08781) | **DG** | E | WSGW | CF |
|-------|---------|--------|---|------|-----|
| 09204 | (08717) | **DG** | E | WSNE | IM |
| 09205 | (08620) | **DG** | E | WSSC | ML |

## CLASS 20 ENGLISH ELECTRIC Bo-Bo

**Built:** 1957–1968 by English Electric Company at Vulcan Foundry, Newton le Willows or by Robert Stephenson & Hawthorn at Darlington.
**Engine:** English Electric 8SVT Mk. II of 746 kW (1000 h.p.) at 850 r.p.m.
**Main Generator:** English Electric 819/3C.
**Traction Motors:** English Electric 526/5D or 526/8D.
**Maximum Tractive Effort:** 187 kN (42000 lbf).
**Continuous Tractive Effort:** 111 kN (25000 lbf) at 11 m.p.h.
**Power At Rail:** 574 kW (770 h.p.).   **Train Brakes:** Air & vacuum.
**Brake Force:** 35 t.   **Dimensions:** 14.25 x 2.67 m.
**Weight:** 73.4–73.5 t.   **Wheel Diameter:** 1092 mm.
**Design Speed:** 75 m.p.h.   **Maximum Speed:** 75 m.p.h.
**Fuel Capacity:** 1727 litres.   **RA:** 5.
**Train Supply:** Not equipped.   **Multiple Working:** Blue Star.

Notes:

20113 and 20175 are stored in an industrial estate off Kingmoor Road, Carlisle.

Non-standard liveries:

20088, 20105, 20108, 20113, 20145, 20159 and 20175 are in RFS grey.
20092 is in Central Services grey & red livery.
20132, 20138 and 20215 are as **F0** but with a red solebar stripe.

Originally numbered in series D 8007–8190, 8315–8325.

**Class 20/0. Standard Design.**

| 20016 | **B** | DR | XHSS | LT |
|-------|-------|-----|------|-----|
| 20032 | **B** | DR | XHSS | LT |
| 20057 | **B** | DR | XHSS | LT |
| 20066 | **B** | DR | XHSS | LT |
| 20072 | **B** | DR | XHSS | LT |
| 20073 | **B** | DR | XHSS | LT |
| 20081 | **B** | DR | XHSS | LT |
| 20088 | **0** | DR | XHSS | LT |
| 20092 | **0** | DR | XHSS | LT |
| 20094 | **B** | DR | XHSS | ZH |
| 20096 | **B** | HN | HNRS | BH |
| 20105 | **0** | DR | XHSS | LT |
| 20108 | **0** | DR | XHSS | LT |
| 20113 | **0** | DR | XHSS | KM |
| 20119 | **B** | HN | HNRS | TT |
| 20121 | **B** | DR | XHSS | LT |
| 20132 | **0** | DR | XHSS | LT |
| 20135 | **B** | DR | XHSS | ZH |
| 20138 | **0** | DR | XHSS | LT |
| 20145 | **0** | DR | XHSS | LT |
| 20159 | **0** | DR | XHSS | LT |

| 20168 | **B** | HN | HNRS | BH |
| 20175 | **0** | DR | XHSS | KM |
| 20215 | **0** | DR | XHSS | LT |

**Class 20/3. Direct Rail Services refurbished locos.** Details as Class 20/0 except:

**Refurbished:** 1995–1996 by Brush Traction at Loughborough (20301–20305) or 1997–98 by RFS(E) at Doncaster (20306–20315). Disc indicators or headcode panels removed.

| | | |
|---|---|---|
| **Train Brakes:** Air. | **Maximum Speed:** 75 m.p.h. | |
| **Brake Force:** 31 t. | **Fuel Capacity:** 2900 (+ 4909) litres. | |

**Multiple Working:** Blue Star (20301–305 at nose end only).

| 20301 | (20047) | + | **DR** | DR XHSD | KM | Max Joule 1958–1999 |
| 20302 | (20084) | | **DR** | DR XHSD | KM | |
| 20303 | (20127) | + | **DR** | DR XHSD | KM | |
| 20304 | (20120) | | **DR** | DR XHSD | KM | |
| 20305 | (20095) | | **DR** | DR XHSD | KM | |
| 20306 | (20131) | + | **DR** | DR XHSD | KM | |
| 20307 | (20128) | + | **DR** | DR XHSD | KM | |
| 20308 | (20187) | + | **DR** | DR XHSD | KM | |
| 20309 | (20075) | + | **DR** | DR XHSD | KM | |
| 20310 | (20190) | + | **DR** | DR XHSD | KM | |
| 20311 | (20102) | + | **DR** | DR XHSD | KM | |
| 20312 | (20042) | + | **DR** | DR XHSD | KM | |
| 20313 | (20194) | + | **DR** | DR XHSD | KM | |
| 20314 | (20117) | + | **DR** | DR XHSD | KM | |
| 20315 | (20104) | + | **DR** | DR XHSD | KM | |

**Class 20/9. Direct Rail Services (former Hunslet-Barclay) refurbished locos.** Details as Class 20/0 except:

**Refurbished:** 1989 by Hunslet-Barclay at Kilmarnock.
**Train Brakes:** Air.                         **Fuel Capacity:** 1727 (+ 4727) litres.

| 20901 | (20041) | | **DR** | DR XHSS | KM |
| 20902 | (20060) | + | **DR** | DR XHSS | ZH |
| 20903 | (20083) | + | **DR** | DR XHSS | KM |
| 20904 | (20101) | | **DR** | DR XHSS | KM |
| 20905 | (20225) | + | **DR** | DR XHSD | KM |
| 20906 | (20219) | | **DR** | DR XHSS | CP |

# CLASS 31 BRUSH/ENGLISH ELECTRIC A1A-A1A

**Built:** 1958–1962 by Brush Traction at Loughborough.
**Engine:** English Electric 12SVT of 1100 kW (1470 h.p.) at 850 r.p.m.
**Main Generator:** Brush TG160-48.      **Traction Motors:** Brush TM73-68.
**Maximum Tractive Effort:** 160 kN (35900 lbf).
**Continuous Tractive Effort:** 83 kN (18700 lbf) at 23.5 m.p.h.

| | |
|---|---|
| **Power At Rail:** 872 kW (1170 h.p.). | **Train Brakes:** Air & vacuum. |
| **Brake Force:** 49 t. | **Dimensions:** 17.30 x 2.67 m. |
| **Weight:** 106.7–111 t. | **Wheel Diameter:** 1092/1003 mm. |
| **Design Speed:** 90 m.p.h. | **Maximum Speed:** 90 m.p.h. |
| **Fuel Capacity:** 2409 litres. | **RA:** 5 or 6. |

**Train Supply:** Not equipped.          **Multiple Working:** Blue Star.

Originally numbered D 5520–5699, 5800–5862 (not in order).

**Non-standard livery/numbering:**

31110  Carries number D5528.
31301  As **FO** but with a red solebar stripe.

**Class 31/1. Standard Design.** RA: 5.

| | | | | | |
|---|---|---|---|---|---|
| 31102 | **CE** | NR | QADD | CS | (S) |
| 31105 | **F** | NR | QADD | DY | (S) |
| 31106 | **FR** | HJ | SDFR | DF | SPALDING TOWN |
| 31107 | **CE** | NR | QADD | DY | (S) |
| 31110 a | **G** | E | WMOC | BH | TRACTION magazine |
| 31113 | **CE** | E | WNZX | OC | |
| 31128 | **FR** | FR | SDFR | DF | CHARYBDIS |
| 31154 | **CE** | FR | SDXL | DY | |
| 31190 | **RK** | FR | SDFR | DF | GRYPHON |
| 31200 | **F** | NR | QADD | CS | (S) |
| 31206 | **CE** | CD | CROL | LB | |
| 31207 | **CE** | E | WNZX | OC | |
| 31233 | **CE** | NR | QADD | DF | (S) |
| 31275 | **F** | HN | HNRS | CS | |
| 31285 | **Y** | NR | QADD | DF | |
| 31296 | **F** | E | WNZX | CP | |
| 31301 | **O** | FR | SDXL | MQ | |
| 31306 | **CE** | E | WNZX | OC | |
| 31308 | **CE** | E | WNZX | OC | |
| 31319 | **F** | NR | QADD | CS | (S) |

**Class 31/4. Electric Train Supply equipment.** RA: 6.
**Class 31/5. Train Heating Equipment isolated.** RA6.

| | | | | | |
|---|---|---|---|---|---|
| 31407 | **ML** | FR | SDXL | BH | |
| 31410 | **RR** | HN | HNRS | CS | |
| 31411 | **DG** | FR | SDXL | BH | |
| 31412 | **CE** | FR | SDXL | BH | |
| 31514 | **CE** | E | WNXX | OC | |
| 31415 | **B** | FR | SDXL | MQ | |
| 31417 | **DG** | FR | SDXL | BH | |
| 31420 | **IM** | E | WNXX | OC | |
| 31422 | **IM** | FR | SDXL | TM | |
| 31423 | **IM** | FR | SDXL | MQ | |
| 31424 | **CE** | FR | SDXL | BH | |
| 31426 | **CE** | FR | SDXL | MQ | |
| 31427 | **B** | E | WNXX | OC | |
| 31433 | **CE** | FR | SDXL | BH | |
| 31437 | **CE** | FR | SDXL | MQ | |
| 31439 | **RR** | FR | SDXL | MQ | |
| 31449 | **CE** | FR | SDXL | TM | |
| 31452 | **FR** | FR | SDFR | DF | MINOTAUR |
| 31454 | **I** | FR | SDFR | DF | |

| 31458 | CE | FR | SDXL | TM |
|-------|-----|-----|------|-----|
| 31459 | FR | FR | SDFR | DF | CERBERUS |
| 31460 | B | FR | SDXL | BH |
| 31461 | DG | FR | SDXL | DF |
| 31462 | DG | FR | SDXL | TM |
| 31465 | RR | E | WNXX | OC |
| 31466 a | E | E | WNXX | OC |
| 31468 | FR | FR | SDFR | DF | HYDRA |

**Class 31/6. ETS through wiring and controls.** RA: 5.

| 31601 (31186) | RK | FR | SDFR | DF | BLETCHLEY PARK 'STATION X' |
|---------------|-----|-----|------|-----|-----|
| 31602 (31191) | FR | FR | SDFR | DF | CHIMAERA |

# CLASS 33          BRCW/SULZER          Bo-Bo

**Built:** 1960–1962 by the Birmingham Railway Carriage & Wagon Company at Smethwick.
**Engine:** Sulzer 8LDA28 of 1160 kW (1550 h.p.) at 750 r.p.m.
**Main Generator:** Crompton Parkinson CG391B1.
**Traction Motors:** Crompton Parkinson C171C2.
**Maximum Tractive Effort:** 200 kN (45000 lbf).
**Continuous Tractive Effort:** 116 kN (26000 lbf) at 17.5 m.p.h.
**Power At Rail:** 906 kW (1215 h.p.).　**Train Brakes:** Air & vacuum.
**Brake Force:** 35 t.　**Dimensions:** 15.47 x 2.82 (2.64 m. 33/2).
**Weight:** 77.7 t.　**Wheel Diameter:** 1092 mm.
**Design Speed:** 85 m.p.h.　**Maximum Speed:** 85 m.p.h.
**Fuel Capacity:** 3410 litres.　**RA:** 6.
**Train Supply:** Electric, index 48 (750 V DC only).
**Multiple Working:** Blue Star.

Originally numbered in series D 6500–97 but not in order.

#### Non-standard liveries/numbering:

33046 All over mid-blue.
33051 Also carries number 6569.
33109 Also carries number D6525.
33116 Also carries number D6535.
33208 Also carries number D6593.

#### Class 33/0. Standard Design.

| 33002 | CE | DR | XHSS | LT |
|-------|-----|-----|------|-----|
| 33008 | G | DR | XHSS | LT |
| 33019 | CE | FR | SDXL | DF |
| 33021 | FR | WF | SDFR | DF | Eastleigh |
| 33023 | B | DR | XHSS | ZH |
| 33025 | DR | DR | XHSD | KM |
| 33029 | B | DR | XHSS | DF |
| 33030 | DR | DR | XHSD | KM |
| 33046 | O | FR | SDXL | DF |
| 33053 | F | DR | XHSS | LT |
| 33057 | CE | DR | XHSS | LT |

**Class 33/1. Fitted with Buckeye Couplings & SR Multiple Working Equipment for use with SR EMUs, TC stock & Class 73.** Also fitted with flashing light adaptor for use on Weymouth Quay line.

| | | | | | | |
|---|---|---|---|---|---|---|
| 33103 | b | **FR** | CM | SDFR | DF | SWORDFISH |
| 33108 | b | **FR** | 11 | SDFR | DF | VAMPIRE |
| 33109 | b | **B** | 71 | MBDL | RL | Captain Bill Smith RNR |
| 33116 | b | **B** | E | WNZX | OC | |

**Class 33/2. Built to Former Loading Gauge of Tonbridge–Battle Line.** All equipped with slow speed control.

| | | | | | |
|---|---|---|---|---|---|
| 33202 | **FR** | FR | SDFR | DF | METEOR |
| 33203 | **F** | DR | XHSS | LT | |
| 33207 | **DR** | DR | XHSD | KM | |
| 33208 | **G** | 71 | MBDL | RL | |

# CLASS 37          ENGLISH ELECTRIC          Co-Co

**Built:** 1960–1965 by English Electric Company at Vulcan Foundry, Newton le Willows or by Robert Stephenson & Hawthorn at Darlington.
**Engine:** English Electric 12CSVT of 1300 kW (1750 h.p.) at 850 r.p.m.
**Main Generator:** English Electric 822/10G.
**Traction Motors:** English Electric 538/A.
**Maximum Tractive Effort:** 245 kN (55500 lbf).
**Continuous Tractive Effort:** 156 kN (35000 lbf) at 13.6 m.p.h.
**Power At Rail:** 932 kW (1250 h.p.).     **Train Brakes:** Air & vacuum.
**Brake Force:** 50 t.                      **Dimensions:** 18.75 x 2.74 m.
**Weight:** 102.8–108.4 t.                  **Wheel Diameter:** 1092 mm.
**Design Speed:** 90 m.p.h.                 **Maximum Speed:** 80 m.p.h.
**Fuel Capacity:** 4046 (+ 7678) litres.    **RA:** 5 (§ 6).
**Train Supply:** Not equipped.             **Multiple Working:** Blue Star.

Originally numbered D 6600–8, 6700–6999 (not in order).

**Non-standard liveries/numbering:**

37131 Also carries number 6831.
37137 Has been used for paint trials.
37351 Carries number 37002 on one side only.
37402 Light grey lower bodyside with dark grey upper bodyside.
37403 Carries number D6607.
37906 As **F0** but with a red solebar stripe.

**Class 37/0. Standard Design.** Details as above.

| | | | | | | |
|---|---|---|---|---|---|---|
| 37010 | a | **CE** | E | WNYX | SP | |
| 37013 | | **ML** | DR | XHSS | LB | |
| 37019 | | **F** | DR | XHSS | LB | |
| 37023 | | **ML** | E | WNXX | OC | Stratford TMD |
| 37029 | § | **DR** | DR | XHCK | KM | |
| 37037 | a | **F** | HN | HNRS | SP | |
| 37038 | | **DR** | DR | XHCK | KM | |
| 37040 | | **E** | E | WNYX | SP | |

| 37042 | + | E | E | WKAC | OC | |
|---|---|---|---|---|---|---|
| 37046 | a | CE | E | WKGF | TY | |
| 37047 | + | ML | E | WKAC | OC | |
| 37051 | | E | E | WKAC | OC | |
| 37055 | + | ML | E | WNXX | TE | |
| 37057 | + | E | E | WKAC | OC | Viking |
| 37058 | a+ | CE | E | WKGF | TY | |
| 37059 | a+ | DR | DR | XHCK | KM | |
| 37065 | + | ML | E | WKAC | OC | |
| 37068 | | F | DR | XHSS | LB | |
| 37069 | a+ | DR | DR | XHCK | KM | |
| 37071 | a+ | CE | E | WNYX | SP | |
| 37072 | | DG | HN | HNRS | BH | |
| 37074 | a+ | ML | E | WNYX | SP | |
| 37077 | a | ML | E | WKGF | TY | |
| 37078 | | F | HN | HNRS | SP | |
| 37079 | | F | HN | HNRS | BH | |
| 37087 | | HN | HN | HNRL | BH | Vulcan Avro B1 & B2 |
| 37095 | | CE | HN | HNRS | CS | |
| 37100 | a | F | E | WNXX | TY | |
| 37109 | | E | E | WKAC | OC | |
| 37114 | r+ | E | E | WKSN | TO | City of Worcester |
| 37116 | + | B | E | WNYX | EH | Sister Dora |
| 37131 | + | F | E | WNYX | SP | |
| 37133 | a | CE | HN | HNRS | CS | |
| 37137 | | 0 | HN | HNRS | TT | |
| 37139 | | F | X | WNSO | TE | |
| 37141 | | CE | HN | HNRS | CS | |
| 37146 | a | CE | E | WNXX | TY | |
| 37152 | | I | E | WNYX | ML | |
| 37162 | + | DG | E | WNYX | SP | |
| 37165 | a+ | CE | HN | HNRS | CS | |
| 37170 | a | CE | E | WNYX | SP | |
| 37174 | a | E | E | WKAC | OC | |
| 37175 | a | CE | E | WMOC | OC | |
| 37178 | + | F | E | WNYX | EH | |
| 37185 | + | CE | E | WNYX | SP | |
| 37188 | | CE | X | WNSO | CS | |
| 37194 | | HN | HN | HNRL | BH | NEIL WEBSTER 1957–2001 |
| 37196 | a | CE | E | WKGF | TY | |
| 37197 | | IR | IR | MBDL | BQ | |
| 37198 | + | ML | E | WNXX | TT | |
| 37201 | | CE | HN | HNRS | BH | |
| 37203 | | ML | E | WKAC | OC | |
| 37212 | + | F | E | WNZX | EH | |
| 37214 | | F | HN | HNRS | BH | |
| 37216 | + | ML | E | WNTR | TO | |
| 37217 | + | B | X | WNSO | AY | |
| 37218 | | DR | DR | XHCK | KM | |
| 37219 | | ML | E | WNXX | EH | |
| 37220 | + | E | E | WNXX | TT | |

| | | | | | |
|---|---|---|---|---|---|
| 37221 | a | **F** | E | WKGF | TY |
| 37222 | | **F** | HN | HNRS | CS |
| 37225 | + | **F** | E | WNZX | SP |
| 37229 | § | **DR** | DR | XHCK | KM |
| 37230 | + | **CE** | E | WNYX | TT |
| 37235 | | **F** | IR | MBDL | BQ |
| 37238 | a+ | **F** | E | WKGF | TY |
| 37242 | | **ML** | HN | HNRS | BH |
| 37248 | + | **ML** | E | WKAD | CD |
| 37250 | a+ | **F** | E | WKGF | TY |
| 37259 | | **DR** | DR | XHCK | KM |
| 37261 | a+ | **F** | IR | MBDL | BQ |
| 37262 | + | **DG** | DR | XHSS | LB |
| 37263 | | **CE** | E | WNZX | EH |
| 37275 | + | **B** | E | WNYX | TT |
| 37293 | a+ | **ML** | E | WKGF | TY |
| 37294 | a+ | **CE** | E | WKSN | TO |
| 37298 | a+ | **E** | E | WNYX | SP |
| 37308 | r+ | **B** | E | WKSN | TO |

Midland Railway Centre

**Class 37/3. Re-geared (CP7) bogies.** Details as Class 37/0 except:

**Maximum Tractive Effort:** 250 kN (56180 lbf).
**Continuous Tractive Effort:** 184 kN (41250 lbf) at 11.4 m.p.h.
**Design Speed:** 80 m.p.h.

| | | | | | |
|---|---|---|---|---|---|
| 37334 | | **F** | DR | XHSS | LB |
| 37344 | | **F** | DR | XHSS | LB |
| 37351 | + | **CE** | E | WNXX | CD |
| 37358 | + | **F** | X | WNSO | IM |
| 37359 | | **F** | HN | HNRS | CS |
| 37370 | a | **E** | E | WNYX | SP |
| 37372 | | **ML** | E | WKAD | CD |
| 37375 | a+ | **ML** | E | WKAD | CD |
| 37376 | a+ | **F** | E | WNYX | SP |
| 37377 | + | **CE** | E | WKGF | EH |
| 37379 | a | **ML** | E | WNXX | EH |
| 37383 | + | **ML** | DR | XHSS | CP |
| 37384 | | **CE** | DR | XHSS | LB |

Ipswich WRD Quality Approved

**Class 37/4. Refurbished with electric train supply equipment.** Main generator replaced by alternator. Re-geared (CP7) bogies. Details as Class 37/0 except:

**Main Alternator:** Brush BA1005A.
**Maximum Tractive Effort:** 256 kN (57440 lbf).
**Continuous Tractive Effort:** 184 kN (41250 lbf) at 11.4 m.p.h.
**Power At Rail:** 935 kW (1254 h.p.).
**Weight:** 107 t.
**Design Speed:** 80 m.p.h.
**Fuel Capacity:** 7678 litres.
**Train Supply:** Electric, index 38.

**Note:** 37405, 37408 and 37411 are on hire from the WKAD pool to pool WKHF, for use on the Arriva Trains Northern loco-hauled services.

| | | | | | |
|---|---|---|---|---|---|
| 37401 | r | **GS** | E | WKBM | ML | The Royal Scotsman |
| 37402 | | **O** | E | WKCK | CF | Bont Y Bermo |
| 37403 | a | **G** | E | WNYX | MG | |
| 37405 | | **E** | E | WKAD | CD | |
| 37406 | r | **E** | E | WKBM | ML | The Saltire Society |
| 37407 | | **F** | E | WNXX | SP | |
| 37408 | | **E** | E | WKAD | CD | Loch Rannoch |
| 37409 | | **F** | E | WNSS | ML | |
| 37410 | r | **E** | E | WKBM | ML | |
| 37411 | | **E** | E | WKAD | CD | The Scottish Railway Preservation Society |
| 37412 | | **F** | E | WNSS | CF | Driver John Elliott |
| 37413 | | **E** | E | WNXX | CF | |
| 37414 | | **RR** | E | WNYX | SP | |
| 37415 | | **E** | E | WNSS | CF | |
| 37416 | r | **E** | E | WKBM | ML | Sir Robert McAlpine/Concrete Bob |
| 37417 | a | **E** | E | WKCK | CF | East Lancashire Railway |
| 37418 | r | **E** | E | WKBM | ML | |
| 37419 | r | **E** | E | WKBM | ML | East Lancashire Railway |
| 37420 | | **RR** | E | WNXX | CD | The Scottish Hosteller |
| 37421 | r | **E** | E | WKBM | ML | |
| 37422 | | **E** | E | WKCK | CF | Cardiff Canton |
| 37423 | | **F** | IR | MBDL | BQ | |
| 37424 | | **F** | E | WNYX | ML | |
| 37425 | | **E** | E | WKCK | CF | |
| 37426 | r§ | **E** | E | WKSN | TO | |
| 37427 | r | **E** | E | WKBM | ML | |
| 37428 | r | **GS** | E | WKBM | ML | Loch Long/Loch Awe |
| 37429 | | **RR** | E | WNXX | TT | |
| 37430 | a | **F** | E | WNYX | ML | Cwmbrân |

**Class 37/5. Refurbished without train supply equipment. Main generator replaced by alternator. Re-geared (CP7) bogies.**
Details as Class 37/4 except:
**Maximum Tractive Effort:** 248 kN (55590 lbf).
**Weight:** 106.1–110.0) t.

| | | | | | |
|---|---|---|---|---|---|
| 37503 | r§ | **E** | E | WKSN | TO | |
| 37505 | a§ | **F** | E | WKGF | AY | British Steel Workington |
| 37509 | a§ | **F** | E | WNXX | CF | |
| 37510 | a | **I** | HN | HNRS | BH | |
| 37513 | as§ | **LH** | E | WNXX | OC | |
| 37515 | as | **HN** | HN | HNRS | BH | |
| 37516 | s§ | **LH** | E | WKSN | TO | |
| 37517 | as§ | **LH** | E | WKSN | TO | |
| 37518 | a§ | **F** | E | WKGF | AY | |
| 37519 | | **F** | E | WKGF | EH | |
| 37520 | r§ | **E** | E | WNXX | CD | |
| 37521 | r§ | **E** | E | WKSN | TO | English China Clays |

**Class 37/6. Originally refurbished for Nightstar services.** Main generator replaced by alternator, re-geared bogies and UIC jumpers. Details as Class 37/5 except:

**Maximum Speed:** 90 m.p.h.                **Train Brake:** Air.
**Train Supply:** Not equipped, but electric through wired.
**Multiple Working:** TDM († plus Blue Star).

| | | | | | |
|---|---|---|---|---|---|
| 37601 | **EP** | EU | GPSV | OC | |
| 37602 † | **DR** | DR | XHCK | KM | |
| 37603 | **EP** | EU | GPSV | OC | |
| 37604 | **EP** | EU | GPSV | OC | |
| 37605 † | **DR** | DR | XHCK | KM | |
| 37606 † | **DR** | DR | XHCK | KM | |
| 37607 † | **DR** | DR | XHCK | KM | |
| 37608 † | **DR** | DR | XHCK | KM | |
| 37609 † | **DR** | DR | XHCK | KM | |
| 37610 † | **DR** | DR | XHCK | KM | The MALCOLM Group |
| 37611 † | **DR** | DR | XHCK | KM | |
| 37612 † | **DR** | DR | XHCK | KM | |

**Class 37/5 continued.**

| | | | | | |
|---|---|---|---|---|---|
| 37667 rs§ | **E** | E | WKSN | TO | Meldon Quarry Centenary |
| 37668 s§ | **E** | E | WKSN | TO | |
| 37669 r§ | **E** | E | WKSN | TO | |
| 37670 r§ | **E** | E | WKSN | TO | St. Blazey T&RS Depot |
| 37671 a | **F** | E | WKGF | TY | |
| 37672 as | **F** | E | WNXX | TE | |
| 37673 § | **F** | E | WNXX | TE | |
| 37674 § | **F** | E | WKSN | TO | Saint Blaise Church 1445–1995 |
| 37675 as§ | **F** | E | WKSN | TO | Margam TMD |
| 37676 a§ | **F** | E | WKSN | TO | |
| 37677 a§ | **F** | E | WNTR | IM | |
| 37678 a§ | **F** | E | WNXX | BS | |
| 37679 a§ | **F** | E | WKGF | AY | |
| 37680 a§ | **F** | E | WNXX | TE | |
| 37682 r§ | **E** | E | WKSN | TO | Hartlepool Pipe Mill |
| 37683 a | **F** | E | WNXX | TE | |
| 37684 ar§ | **E** | E | WKSN | TO | Peak National Park |
| 37685 a§ | **I** | E | WKSN | TO | |
| 37686 a | **F** | E | WNYX | SP | |
| 37688 § | **E** | E | WNTR | SR | |
| 37689 a§ | **F** | E | WKSN | TO | |
| 37692 s§ | **F** | E | WKSN | TO | Didcot Depot |
| 37693 as | **F** | E | WKGF | TY | |
| 37694 § | **E** | E | WKSN | TO | |
| 37695 s§ | **E** | E | WKSN | TO | |
| 37696 as | **F** | E | WKGF | TY | |
| 37697 | **E** | E | WNYX | SP | |
| 37698 a§ | **LH** | E | WKSN | TO | |

**Class 37/7. Refurbished locos. Main generator replaced by alternator. Re-geared (CP7) bogies.** Ballast weights added.
Details as Class 37/5 except:
**Main Alternator:** GEC G564AZ (37796–803) Brush BA1005A (others).
**Maximum Tractive Effort:** 276 kN (62000 lbf).
**Weight:** 120 t.       **RA:** 7.

| | | | | | |
|---|---|---|---|---|---|
| 37701 | as F | E | WKGF | OC | |
| 37702 | s GIF | E | WKGS | ES | |
| 37703 | GIF | E | WKGS | ES | |
| 37704 | s E | E | WNYX | CF | |
| 37705 | F | E | WKGF | ML | |
| 37706 | E | E | WKSN | TO | |
| 37707 | E | E | WKAD | CD | |
| 37708 | a F | E | WNXX | DR | |
| 37709 | § F | E | WKSN | TO | |
| 37710 | § LH | E | WKSN | TO | |
| 37711 | F | E | WNYX | SP | |
| 37712 | a E | E | WKSN | TO | |
| 37713 | LH | HN | HNRS | CD | |
| 37714 | a GIF | E | WKGS | ES | |
| 37715 | F | E | WNYX | SP | |
| 37716 | GIF | E | WKGS | ES | |
| 37717 | E | E | WKAD | CD | Berwick Middle School |
| | | | | | Railsafe Trophy Winners 1998 |
| 37718 | GIF | E | WKGS | ES | |
| 37719 | a F | E | WKGF | OC | |
| 37796 | as F | E | WKGF | TY | |
| 37797 | s E | E | WNSS | CD | |
| 37798 | ML | E | WKAD | CD | |
| 37799 | as GIF | E | WKGS | ES | |
| 37800 | a GIF | E | WKGS | ES | |
| 37801 | s GIF | E | WKGS | ES | |
| 37803 | a ML | E | WNXX | TY | |
| 37883 | GIF | E | WKGS | ES | |
| 37884 | GIF | E | WKGS | ES | |
| 37886 | E | E | WKAD | CD | Sir Dyfed/County of Dyfed |
| 37887 | s F | E | WKGF | IM | |
| 37888 | GIF | E | WKGS | ES | |
| 37889 | F | HN | HNRS | CD | |
| 37890 | a F | E | WKAD | CD | |
| 37891 | a F | E | WKGF | TY | |
| 37892 | F | E | WKGF | OC | Ripple Lane |
| 37893 | E | E | WKAD | CD | |
| 37894 | as F | E | WKGF | TY | |
| 37895 | s§ E | E | WKSN | TO | |
| 37896 | s§ F | E | WKSN | TO | |
| 37897 | s F | E | WNXX | BS | |
| 37898 | s F | E | WNYX | MG | |

**Class 37/9. Refurbished locos. New power unit. Main generator replaced by alternator. Ballast weights added.** Details as Class 37/4 except:

**Engine:** Mirrlees MB275T of 1340 kW (1800 h.p.) at 1000 r.p.m. (§ Ruston RK270T of 1340 kW (1800 h.p.) at 900 r.p.m.).
**Train supply:** Not equipped.
**Main Alternator:** Brush BA1005A (ç GEC G564AZ).
**Maximum Tractive Effort:** 279 kN (62680 lbf).
**Continuous Tractive Effort:** 184 kN (41250 lbf) at 11.4 m.p.h.
**Weight:** 120 t.                                        **RA:** 7.

| | | | | |
|---|---|---|---|---|
| 37902 | F | DR | XHSS | KM |
| 37903 | F | HN | HNRS | CD |
| 37904 | F | HN | HNRS | CS |
| 37905 §s | F | E | WNYX | IM |
| 37906 §s | F0 | E | WMOC | KR |

# CLASS 40          ENGLISH ELECTRIC          1Co-Co1

**Built:** 1958–1962 by the English Electric Co. at Vulcan Foundry, Newton le Willows.
**Engine:** English Electric 16SVT Mk2 of 1490 kW (2000 h.p.) at 850 r.p.m.
**Main Generator:** English Electric 822.
**Traction Motors:** English Electric 526/5D.
**Maximum Tractive Effort:** 231 kN (52000 lbf).
**Continuous Tractive Effort:** 137 kN (30900 lbf) at 18.8 m.p.h.

| | |
|---|---|
| **Power At Rail:** 1160 kW (1550 h.p.). | **Train Brakes:** Air & vacuum. |
| **Brake Force:** 51 t. | **Dimensions:** 21.18 x 2.78 m. |
| **Weight:** 132 t. | **Wheel Diameter:** 914/1143 mm. |
| **Design Speed:** 90 m.p.h. | **Maximum Speed:** 90 m.p.h. |
| **Fuel Capacity:** 3250 litres. | **RA:** 6. |
| **Train Supply:** Steam. | **Multiple Working:** Not equipped. |

Also carries original number D 345.

| 40145 | B | 40 | MBDL | BQ |
|---|---|---|---|---|

# CLASS 43          BREL/PAXMAN          Bo-Bo

**Built:** 1976–1982 by BREL at Crewe Works.
**Engine:** Paxman Valenta 12RP200L of 1680 kW (2250 h.p.) at 1500 r.p.m.
(* Paxman 12VP185 of 1680 kW (2250 h.p.) at 1500 r.p.m.).
**Main Alternator:** Brush BA1001B.
**Traction Motors:** Brush TMH68–46 or GEC G417AZ, frame mounted.
**Maximum Tractive Effort:** 80 kN (17980 lbf).
**Continuous Tractive Effort:** 46 kN (10340 lbf) at 64.5 m.p.h.

| | |
|---|---|
| **Power At Rail:** 1320 kW (1770 h.p.). | **Train Brakes:** Air. |
| **Brake Force:** 35 t. | **Dimensions:** 17.79 x 2.71 m. |
| **Weight:** 70.25 t. | **Wheel Diameter:** 1020 mm. |
| **Design Speed:** 125 m.p.h. | **Maximum Speed:** 125 m.p.h. |
| **Fuel Capacity:** 4500 litres. | **RA:** 5. |

**Train Supply:** Three-phase electric.
**Multiple Working:** Within class, jumpers at non-driving end only.
**Note:** † = Buffer fitted.

| Number | | | | | Name |
|---|---|---|---|---|---|
| 43002 | FG | A | IWRP | PM | TECHNIQUEST |
| 43003 | FG | A | IWRP | PM | |
| 43004 | FP | A | IWRP | PM | Borough of Swindon |
| 43005 | FP | A | SCXL | NL | |
| 43006 | GN | A | IECP | EC | Kingdom of Fife |
| 43007 | MN | A | IMLP | NL | |
| 43008 | GN | A | IECP | EC | City of Aberdeen |
| 43009 | FP | A | SCXL | NL | |
| 43010 | FP | A | IWRP | PM | |
| 43012 | FP | A | IWRP | PM | |
| 43013 † | Y | P | QCAR | DY | |
| 43014 † | Y | P | QCAR | DY | |
| 43015 | FP | A | IWRP | PM | |
| 43016 | FG | A | IWRP | PM | Peninsula Medical School |
| 43017 | FG | A | IWRP | LA | |
| 43018 | FG | A | IWRP | LA | The Red Cross |
| 43019 | FG | A | IWRP | LA | City of Swansea/Dinas Abertawe |
| 43020 | FG | A | IWRP | LA | John Grooms |
| 43021 | FG | A | IWRP | LA | |
| 43022 | FG | A | IWRP | PM | |
| 43023 | FG | A | IWRP | PM | County of Cornwall |
| 43024 | FG | A | IWRP | PM | |
| 43025 | FG | A | IWRP | PM | Exeter |
| 43026 | FG | A | IWRP | PM | City of Westminster |
| 43027 | FG | A | IWRP | PM | Glorious Devon |
| 43028 | FP | A | IWRP | PM | |
| 43029 | FG | A | IWRP | LA | |
| 43030 | FP | A | IWRP | PM | Christian Lewis Trust |
| 43031 | FG | A | IWRP | PM | |
| 43032 | FG | A | IWRP | PM | The Royal Regiment of Wales |
| 43033 | FG | A | IWRP | PM | Driver Brian Cooper |
| | | | | | 15 June 1947–5 October 1999 |
| 43034 | FP | A | IWRP | PM | The Black Horse |
| 43035 | FP | A | IWRP | PM | |
| 43036 | FP | A | IWRP | PM | |
| 43037 | FP | A | IWRP | PM | |
| 43038 | GN | A | IECP | EC | |
| 43039 | GN | A | IECP | EC | The Royal Dragoon Guards |
| 43040 | FG | A | IWRP | PM | Bristol St. Philips Marsh |
| 43041 | FG | A | IWRP | PM | City of Discovery |
| 43042 | FG | A | IWRP | PM | |
| 43043 * | MM | P | IMLP | NL | LEICESTERSHIRE COUNTY CRICKET CLUB |
| 43044 * | MM | P | IMLP | NL | Borough of Kettering |
| 43045 * | MM | P | IMLP | NL | |
| 43046 * | MM | P | IMLP | NL | Royal Philharmonic |
| 43047 * | MM | P | IMLP | NL | |
| 43048 * | MM | P | IMLP | NL | |
| 43049 * | MM | P | IMLP | NL | Neville Hill |
| 43050 * | MM | P | IMLP | NL | |
| 43051 | MN | P | IMLP | NL | |

| 43052 | * | MM | P | IMLP | NL |                          |
|-------|---|----|---|------|----|---------------------------|
| 43053 |   | MM | P | IMLP | NL | Leeds United              |
| 43054 |   | MM | P | IMLP | NL |                           |
| 43055 | * | MM | P | IMLP | NL | Sheffield Star            |
| 43056 |   | MM | P | IMLP | NL |                           |
| 43057 |   | MM | P | IMLP | NL |                           |
| 43058 |   | MN | P | IMLP | NL |                           |
| 43059 | * | MM | P | IMLP | NL |                           |
| 43060 | * | MM | P | IMLP | NL | COUNTY OF LEICESTERSHIRE  |
| 43061 | * | MM | P | IMLP | NL |                           |
| 43062 |   | Y  | P | QCAR | DY | Maiden Voyager            |
| 43063 |   | V  | P | IMRL | NL |                           |
| 43064 |   | MM | P | IMLP | NL |                           |
| 43065 | † | V  | P | ICCP | LA | Nottingham Playhouse      |
| 43066 |   | MM | P | IMLP | NL |                           |
| 43067 | † | V  | P | ICCP | LA | The Red Arrows            |
| 43068 | † | V  | P | ICCP | LA |                           |
| 43069 |   | MN | P | IMRL | NL |                           |
| 43070 |   | MN | P | IMRL | NL |                           |
| 43071 |   | MN | P | IMRL | NL |                           |
| 43072 | * | MM | P | IMLP | NL | Derby Etches Park         |
| 43073 | * | MM | P | IMLP | NL |                           |
| 43074 | * | MM | P | IMLP | NL |                           |
| 43075 | * | MM | P | IMLP | NL | THE MASTER CUTLER 1947–1997 |
| 43076 | * | MM | P | IMLP | NL |                           |
| 43077 |   | MM | P | IMLP | NL |                           |
| 43078 |   | MN | P | IMRL | NL |                           |
| 43079 |   | MN | P | IMRL | NL |                           |
| 43080 | † | V  | P | ICCP | LA |                           |
| 43081 |   | MM | P | IMLP | NL |                           |
| 43082 | * | MM | P | IMLP | NL | DERBYSHIRE FIRST          |
| 43083 |   | MM | P | IMLP | NL |                           |
| 43084 | † | V  | P | ICCP | LA | County of Derbyshire      |
| 43085 |   | MN | P | IMLP | NL |                           |
| 43086 |   | V  | P | IMRL | NL |                           |
| 43087 |   | MN | P | IMRL | NL |                           |
| 43088 |   | V  | P | IMRL | NL |                           |
| 43089 |   | MN | P | IMRL | NL |                           |
| 43090 |   | V  | P | SBXL | BR |                           |
| 43091 |   | MN | P | IMRL | NL |                           |
| 43092 |   | V  | P | ICCP | LA | Institution of Mechanical Engineers 150th Anniversary 1847–1997 |
| 43093 |   | V  | P | SBXL | BR |                           |
| 43094 |   | V  | P | ICCP | LA |                           |
| 43095 |   | GN | A | IECP | EC | Perth                     |
| 43096 |   | GN | A | IECP | EC | Stirling Castle           |
| 43097 |   | V  | P | ICCP | LA |                           |
| 43098 |   | V  | P | ICCP | LA | railwaychildren           |
| 43099 |   | V  | P | SBXL | BR |                           |
| 43100 |   | V  | P | SBXL | BR |                           |
| 43101 |   | V  | P | SBXL | LA |                           |

| 43102 | V | P | IMRL | NL | |
|---|---|---|---|---|---|
| 43103 | V | P | SBXL | BR | |
| 43104 | MN | A | IMLP | NL | |
| 43105 | GN | A | IECP | EC | City of Inverness |
| 43106 | GN | A | IECP | EC | Fountains Abbey |
| 43107 | GN | A | IECP | EC | Tayside |
| 43108 | GN | A | IECP | EC | Old Course St. Andrews |
| 43109 | GN | A | IECP | EC | |
| 43110 | GN | A | IECP | EC | Stirlingshire |
| 43111 | GN | A | IECP | EC | Scone Palace |
| 43112 | GN | A | IECP | EC | Doncaster |
| 43113 | GN | A | IECP | EC | |
| 43114 | GN | A | IECP | EC | |
| 43115 | GN | A | IECP | EC | |
| 43116 | GN | A | IECP | EC | |
| 43117 | GN | A | IECP | EC | Bonnie Prince Charlie |
| 43118 | GN | A | IECP | EC | City of Kingston upon Hull |
| 43119 | GN | A | IECP | EC | Harrogate Spa |
| 43120 | GN | A | IECP | EC | |
| 43121 | V | P | ICCP | LA | |
| 43122 | V | P | ICCP | LA | South Yorkshire Metropolitan County |
| 43123 † | V | P | ICCP | LA | |
| 43124 | FP | A | IWRP | LE | |
| 43125 | FP | A | IWRP | LE | Merchant Venturer |
| 43126 | FP | A | IWRP | LE | City of Bristol |
| 43127 | FG | A | IWRP | LE | Sir Peter Parker 1924–2002 |
| | | | | | Cotswold Line 150 |
| 43128 | FP | A | IWRP | LE | |
| 43129 | FP | A | IWRP | LE | |
| 43130 | FG | A | IWRP | LE | Sulis Minerva |
| 43131 | FP | A | IWRP | LE | Sir Felix Pole |
| 43132 | FP | A | IWRP | LE | |
| 43133 | FP | A | IWRP | LE | |
| 43134 | FP | A | IWRP | LE | County of Somerset |
| 43135 | FG | A | IWRP | LE | |
| 43136 | FG | A | IWRP | LE | |
| 43137 | FG | A | IWRP | LE | Newton Abbot 150 |
| 43138 | FG | A | IWRP | LE | |
| 43139 | FP | A | IWRP | LE | |
| 43140 | FG | A | IWRP | LE | |
| 43141 | FG | A | IWRP | LE | |
| 43142 | FG | A | IWRP | LE | |
| 43143 | FP | A | IWRP | LE | |
| 43144 | FP | A | IWRP | LE | |
| 43145 | FP | A | IWRP | LE | |
| 43146 | FG | A | IWRP | LE | |
| 43147 | FP | A | IWRP | LE | |
| 43148 | FP | A | IWRP | LE | |
| 43149 | FP | A | IWRP | LE | B.B.C. Wales Today |
| 43150 | FP | A | IWRP | LE | Bristol Evening Post |
| 43151 | FP | A | IWRP | LE | |

| 43152 | FP | A | IWRP | LE |
| 43153 | V | P | ICCP | LA |

THE ENGLISH RIVIERA
TORQUAY PAIGNTON BRIXHAM

| 43154 | V | P | SBXL | BR |
| 43155 | V | P | IMRL | NL |
| 43156 | V | P | IMRL | NL |
| 43157 | V | P | SBXL | BR |
| 43158 | V | P | IMRL | NL |
| 43159 | MN | P | IMRL | NL |
| 43160 | V | P | SBXL | BR |
| 43161 | MN | P | IMRL | NL |
| 43162 | V | P | IMRL | NL |
| 43163 | FP | A | IWRP | LA |
| 43164 | FP | A | IWRP | LA |
| 43165 * | FG | A | IWRP | LA |
| 43166 | MN | A | IMLP | NL |
| 43167 | GN | A | IECP | EC |
| 43168 * | FP | A | IWRP | LA |
| 43169 * | FP | A | IWRP | LA |
| 43170 * | FP | A | IWRP | LA |
| 43171 | FP | A | IWRP | LA |
| 43172 | FP | A | IWRP | LA |
| 43174 | FP | A | IWRP | LA |
| 43175 | FP | A | IWRP | LA |
| 43176 | FP | A | IWRP | LA |
| 43177 * | FP | A | IWRP | LA |
| 43178 | V | A | IMLP | NL |
| 43179 * | FG | A | IWRP | LA |
| 43180 | MN | P | IMRL | NL |
| 43181 | FP | A | IWRP | LA |

City of Aberdeen

The National Trust
Edward Paxman

Bristol–Bordeaux

University of Exeter

Pride of Laira

Devonport Royal Dockyard
1693–1993

| 43182 | FP | A | IWRP | LA |
| 43183 | FG | A | IWRP | LA |
| 43184 | V | A | IMLP | NL |
| 43185 | FP | A | IWRP | LA |
| 43186 | FP | A | IWRP | LA |
| 43187 | FG | A | IWRP | LA |
| 43188 | FP | A | IWRP | LA |
| 43189 | FP | A | IWRP | LA |
| 43190 | FP | A | IWRP | LA |
| 43191 * | FP | A | IWRP | LA |
| 43192 | FG | A | IWRP | LA |
| 43193 | V | P | IMRL | NL |
| 43194 | V | P | IMRL | NL |
| 43195 | MN | P | IMRL | NL |
| 43196 | V | P | IMRL | NL |
| 43197 | V | P | IMRL | NL |
| 43198 | MN | P | IMRL | NL |

Great Western
Sir Francis Drake

City of Plymouth
RAILWAY HERITAGE TRUST

Seahawk
City of Truro
Plymouth SPIRIT OF DISCOVERY

The Newspaper Society Founded 1836

# CLASS 45             BR/SULZER           1Co-Co1

**Built:** 1963 by BR at Derby Locomotive Works.
**Engine:** Sulzer 12LDA28B of 1860 kW (2500 h.p.) at 750 r.p.m.
**Main Generator:** Crompton-Parkinson CG426 A1.
**Traction Motors:** Crompton-Parkinson C172 A1.
**Maximum Tractive Effort:** 245 kN (55000 lbf).
**Continuous Tractive Effort:** 134 kN (31600 lbf) at 22.3 m.p.h.
**Power At Rail:** 1490 kW (2000 h.p.).      **Train Brakes:** Air & vacuum.
**Brake Force:** 63 t.                        **Dimensions:** 20.70 x 2.78 m.
**Weight:** 140 t.                            **Wheel Diameter:** 914/1143 mm.
**Design Speed:** 90 m.p.h.                   **Maximum Speed:** 90 m.p.h.
**Fuel Capacity:** 3591 litres.               **RA:** 7.
**Train Supply:** Electric.                   **Multiple Working:** Not equipped.

Originally numbered D 61.

45112    **B**    FR    SDMS        DF        THE ROYAL ARMY ORDNANCE CORPS

# CLASS 46             BR/SULZER           1Co-Co1

**Built:** 1963 by BR at Derby Locomotive Works.
**Engine:** Sulzer 12LDA28B of 1860 kW (2500 h.p.) at 750 r.p.m.
**Main Generator:** Brush TG160-60.     **Traction Motors:** Brush TM73-68 Mk3.
**Maximum Tractive Effort:** 245 kN (55000 lbf).
**Continuous Tractive Effort:** 141 kN (31600 lbf) at 22.3 m.p.h.
**Power At Rail:** 1460 kW (1960 h.p.).      **Train Brakes:** Air & vacuum.
**Brake Force:** 63 t.                        **Dimensions:** 20.70 x 2.78 m.
**Weight:** 140 t.                            **Wheel Diameter:** 914/1143 mm.
**Design Speed:** 90 m.p.h.                   **Maximum Speed:** 75 m.p.h.
**Fuel Capacity:** 3591 litres.               **RA:** 7.
**Train Supply:** Not equipped.               **Multiple Working:** Not equipped.

46035    **B**    CN    MBDL        CQ

# CLASS 47             BR/BRUSH/SULZER      Co-Co

**Built:** 1963–1967 by Brush Traction, at Loughborough or by BR at Crewe Works.
**Engine:** Sulzer 12LDA28C of 1920 kW (2580 h.p.) at 750 r.p.m.
**Main Generator:** Brush TG160-60 Mk4 or TM172-50 Mk1.
**Traction Motors:** Brush TM64-68 Mk1 or Mk1A.
**Maximum Tractive Effort:** 267 kN (60000 lbf).
**Continuous Tractive Effort:** 133 kN (30000 lbf) at 26 m.p.h.
**Power At Rail:** 1550 kW (2080 h.p.).      **Train Brakes:** Air.
**Brake Force:** 61 t.                        **Dimensions:** 19.38 x 2.79 m.
**Weight:** 111.5–120.6 t.                    **Wheel Diameter:** 1143 mm.
**Design Speed:** 95 m.p.h.                   **Maximum Speed:** 95 m.p.h. (* 75 m.p.h.).
**Fuel Capacity:** 3273 (+ 5550).
**Train Supply:** Not equipped.
**Multiple Working:** Green Circle (n – not equipped).

Originally numbered in series D 1100–11, 1500–1999 not in order.

**Note:** The DFFT loco has "Dock Mode" slow speed traction control system for working trains from Felixstowe North Container Terminal.

**Non-standard liveries/numbering:**
47004  Also carries number D1524.
47114  As **GG**, but with Freightliner logos.
47145  Dark blue with Railfreight Distribution logos.
47515  Livery **IM** on one side and all-over white on the other side.
47519  Also carries number D1102.
47803  BR experimental Infrastructure livery. Yellow and white with a red stripe.
47829  Special "Police" livery of white with a broad red band outlined in yellow.
47851  Also carries number D1648.
47853  "XP64 blue" with red cabside panels. Also carries number D1733.
47972  BR Central Services livery of red and grey.

**Class 47/0 (Dual braked locos) or Class 47/2 (Air braked locos). Standard Design.** Details as above.

| | | | | | |
|---|---|---|---|---|---|
| 47004 | xn | **GG** | E | WMOC | OC |
| 47033 | | **FE** | CD | CRUR | ZB |
| 47053 | + | **FE** | FR | SDXL | BH |
| 47095 | + | **FE** | HN | HNRS | CS |
| 47114 | + | **0** | FL | DHLT | BA |
| 47145 | + | **0** | FR | SDXL | DF |
| 47146 | + | **FE** | E | WNYX | SP |
| 47150 | *+ | **FL** | FL | DFLH | FD |
| 47156 | | **F** | HN | HNRS | ZH |
| 47157 | + | **FF** | P | DHLT | BA |
| 47186 | + | **FE** | FR | SDXL | KT |
| 47188 | + | **FE** | FR | CROL | CD |
| 47193 | n | **FL** | P | DHLT | BA |
| 47194 | | **F** | DR | XHSS | CS |
| 47197 | n* | **FF** | P | DFLH | FD |
| 47200 | + | **CD** | CD | CRHH | MM | The Fosse Way |
| 47201 | + | **FE** | FR | SDXL | KT |
| 47205 | + | **FF** | FL | DHLT | SZ |
| 47207 | + | **FF** | P | DHLT | SZ |
| 47212 | xn* | **FL** | P | DHLT | CP |
| 47213 | + | **F** | CD | CROL | CD |
| 47217 | + | **FE** | E | WNYX | SP |
| 47219 | + | **FE** | FR | SDXL | KT |
| 47223 | | **F** | HN | HNRS | ZH |
| 47224 | xn* | **F** | P | DHLT | BA |
| 47226 | + | **F** | FR | SDXL | KT |
| 47228 | + | **FE** | FR | SDXL | KT |
| 47229 | + | **F** | FR | SDXL | BH |
| 47234 | + | **FF** | P | SBXL | LB |
| 47236 | + | **FE** | FR | SDXL | CS |
| 47237 | + | **DR** | DR | XHCK | KM |
| 47241 | + | **FE** | E | WNYX | SP |

| 47245 + | FE | WC | MBDL | BH | |
| 47258 + | FL | FL | DHLT | BA | |
| 47270 *n | FL | P | DFLH | FD | Cory Brothers 1842–1992 |
| 47279 *+ | FL | P | DFLH | FD | |
| 47280 + | F | FR | SDXL | KT | |
| 47283 n | FF | DR | XHSS | LT | |
| 47285 + | FE | FR | SDXL | BH | |
| 47287 + | F | FL | DHLT | CD | |
| 47289 *+ | FF | P | DHLT | CP | |
| 47290 + | FF | P | SBXL | LB | |
| 47292 *+ | FL | P | DFLH | FD | |
| 47293 + | FE | FR | SDXL | KT | |
| 47298 + | DR | DR | XHCK | KM | |

**Class 47/3 (Dual braked locos) or Class 47/2 (Air braked locos).**
Details as Class 47/0 except:
**Weight: 113.7 t.**

| 47302 + | FF | FL | DHLT | BA | |
| 47303 *+ | FF | P | DFLM | FD | Freightliner Cleveland |
| 47306 + | FE | E | WMOC | BZ | The Sapper |
| 47307 + | FE | FR | SDXL | KT | |
| 47308 | FF | P | SBXL | LB | |
| 47309 *+ | FF | FL | DFFT | FD | European Rail Operator of The Year |
| 47310 + | FE | E | WNZX | SP | |
| 47313 + | F | FR | SDXL | KT | |
| 47314 + | F | FR | SDXL | KT | |
| 47316 + | CD | CD | CRHH | MM | Cam Peak |
| 47326 + | FE | CD | CROL | ZB | |
| 47328 + | F | E | WNYX | SP | |
| 47331 xns | CE | HN | HNRS | SP | |
| 47334 n | FF | P | DHLT | SZ | |
| 47335 + | F | FR | SDXL | KT | |
| 47338 + | FE | CD | CROL | ZB | |
| 47339 n | FF | P | DHLT | BA | |
| 47345 n | FF | P | SBXL | LB | |
| 47348 + | FE | FR | SDXL | MO | |
| 47353 n | FF | FL | DHLT | BA | |
| 47355 | FB | FR | SDFR | DF | AVOCET |
| 47358 *+ | FF | P | DFLM | FD | |
| 47360 + | FE | FR | SDXL | KT | |
| 47361 + | FF | DR | XHSS | LT | |
| 47363 | F | FR | SDXL | CS | |
| 47365 + | FE | CD | CROL | MM | |
| 47368 xn | F | FR | SDXL | CS | |
| 47370 *+ | FF | P | DHLT | IP | Andrew A Hodgkinson |
| 47371 n | FF | P | SBXL | LB | |
| 47372 n | FF | P | SBXL | LB | |
| 47375 + | FE | FR | SDXL | BH | |

**Class 47/4. Electric Train Supply equipment.**

Details as Class 47/0 except:

**Weight:** 120.4–125.1 t.           **Fuel Capacity:** 3273 (+ 5887) litres.
**Train Supply:** Electric. ETH 66.      **RA:** 7.
**Multiple Working:** Not equipped (m – Green Circle).

| | | | | | |
|---|---|---|---|---|---|
| 47471 | x | **IM** | FR | SDXL | TM |
| 47474 | x | **RG** | E | WNYX | SP |
| 47475 | x | **RX** | CD | CROL | HM |
| 47476 | x | **RG** | E | WNZX | TI |
| 47478 | x | **B** | HN | HNRS | SP |
| 47484 | x | **GW** | DR | XHSS | ZH |
| 47488 | x | **GG** | FR | SDFR | DF |
| 47489 | x | **RG** | FR | SDXL | CS |
| 47492 | x | **RX** | HN | HNRS | CS |
| 47501 | x | **DR** | DR | XHCK | KM |
| 47513 | x | **BL** | E | WNZX | SP |
| 47515 | x | **0** | HN | HNRS | CW |
| 47519 | x+ | **GG** | E | WNYX | SP |
| 47525 | x | **FE** | FR | SDXL | CS |
| 47526 | x | **BL** | FR | SDXL | CS |
| 47528 | x | **IM** | CD | CRUR | HM |
| 47535 | x | **RX** | HN | HNRS | QC |
| 47536 | x | **RX** | E | WNYX | SP |
| 47547 | | **N** | FR | SDXL | TM |
| 47550 | x | **IM** | FR | SDXL | IR |
| 47566 | x | **RX** | E | WNYX | SP |
| 47574 | x | **RG** | FR | SDXL | TM |
| 47575 | x | **RG** | E | WMOC | ML | City of Hereford |
| 47576 | x | **RX** | E | WNYX | SP |
| 47624 | x | **RX** | E | WNYX | SP |
| 47628 | x | **RX** | FR | SDXL | BH |
| 47634 | x | **RG** | E | WNXX | SY | Holbeck |
| 47635 | x | **BL** | E | WHDD | CD | The Lass O' Ballochmyle |
| 47640 | | **RG** | X | WNSO | CD |

**Class 47/7. Fitted with an older form of TDM.**
Details as Class 47/4 except:
**Weight:** 118.7 t. **Fuel Capacity:** 5887 litres.

| | | | | | |
|---|---|---|---|---|---|
| 47701 | x | **FR** | WF | SDFR | DF | Waverley |
| 47702 | x | **V** | E | WNYX | TO | County of Suffolk |
| 47703 | x | **FR** | FR | SDFR | DF | HERMES |
| 47704 | x | **RX** | FR | SDXL | PR |
| 47707 | x | **RX** | FR | SDXL | BH |
| 47709 | x | **FR** | FR | SDFR | DF | DIONYSOS |
| 47710 | x | **FR** | FR | SDFR | DF |
| 47711 | x | **V** | E | WNYX | TI | County of Hertfordshire |
| 47712 | x | **FR** | FR | SDFR | DF | ARTEMIS |
| 47714 | x | **AR** | CD | IANA | NC |
| 47715 | x | **FR** | FR | SDXL | DF | POSEIDON |
| 47716 | x | **RX** | FR | SDXL | MO |
| 47717 | x | **RG** | FR | SDXL | BH |

## Class 47/7. Former Railnet dedicated locos.

All have twin fuel tanks and are fitted with RCH jumper cables for operating with propelling control vehicles (PCVs).

| | | | | | |
|---|---|---|---|---|---|
| 47721 | RX | E | WNXX | TT | Saint Bede |
| 47722 | V | E | WNXX | TT | |
| 47725 | RX | E | WNYX | SP | Bristol Barton Hill |
| 47726 | RX | E | WNXX | TT | Manchester Airport Progress |
| 47727 | E | E | WHCD | CD | Castell Caerffili/Caerphilly Castle |
| 47732 x | RX | E | WHDD | CD | Restormel |
| 47733 | RX | E | WHTN | TO | Eastern Star |
| 47734 | RX | E | WHTN | TO | Crewe Diesel Depot |
| 47736 | RX | E | WNSS | CD | Cambridge Traction & Rolling Stock Depot |
| 47737 | RX | E | WHCD | CD | Resurgent |
| 47739 | RX | E | WHCD | CD | Resourceful |
| 47741 | V | E | WNSS | TT | Resilient |
| 47742 | RX | E | WNXX | TT | The Enterprising Scot |
| 47744 | E | E | WNYX | CD | Royal Mail Cheltenham |
| 47745 x | RX | E | WNYX | TO | Royal London Society for the Blind |
| 47746 | RX | E | WHCD | CD | The Bobby |
| 47747 | E | E | WHCD | CD | Florence Nightingale |
| 47749 | RX | E | WHCD | CD | Atlantic College |
| 47750 | V | E | WHTN | TO | |
| 47756 | RX | E | WNSS | CD | Royal Mail Tyneside |
| 47757 | E | E | WHCD | CD | Capability Brown |
| 47758 x | E | E | WNTR | TO | |
| 47759 | RX | E | WNTR | CD | |
| 47760 | E | E | WHCD | CD | Ribblehead Viaduct |
| 47761 | RX | E | WNTR | CF | |
| 47762 | RX | E | WNXX | SP | |
| 47764 | RX | E | WNYX | SP | |
| 47765 x | RX | E | WNXX | SP | |
| 47766 x | RX | E | WNXX | TT | Resolute |
| 47767 | E | E | WNYX | TO | Mappa Mundi |
| 47768 x | RX | E | WNXX | SP | |
| 47769 | V | E | WNXX | TT | Resolve |
| 47770 | RX | E | WHDD | CD | Reserved |
| 47772 x | RX | E | WHDD | CD | |
| 47773 | E | E | WHCD | CD | The Queen Mother |
| 47774 x | RX | E | WNXX | CD | Poste Restante |
| 47775 x | RX | E | WNXX | CD | |
| 47776 x | RX | E | WHDD | CD | Respected |
| 47777 x | RX | E | WNXX | TO | |
| 47778 | E | E | WHCD | CD | Duke of Edinburgh's Award |
| 47779 | RX | E | WNXX | SP | |
| 47780 | RX | E | WNZX | CD | |
| 47781 | RX | E | WNTR | TO | Isle of Iona |
| 47782 | RX | E | WNTR | OC | |
| 47783 | RX | E | WNXX | CD | Saint Peter |
| 47784 | RX | E | WHCD | CD | Condover Hall |
| 47785 | E | E | WNTR | ML | Fiona Castle |

| 47786 | E | E | WHCD | CD | Roy Castle OBE |
|---|---|---|---|---|---|
| 47787 | E | E | WHCD | CD | Windsor Castle |
| 47789 | RX | E | WHCD | CD | Lindisfarne |
| 47790 | E | E | WHCD | CD | |
| 47791 | RX | E | WHTN | TO | |
| 47792 | E | E | WHCD | CD | Robin Hood |
| 47793 | E | E | WHCD | CD | Christopher Wren |

**Class 47/4 continued. RA6.**

| 47798 | RP | E | WHRD | CD | Prince William |
|---|---|---|---|---|---|
| 47799 | RP | E | WHRD | CD | Prince Henry |
| 47802 + | DR | DR | XHCK | KM | |
| 47803 | 0 | FR | SDXL | PR | |
| 47805 + | V | P | DFLH | FD | |
| 47810 + | V | P | ATLO | WN | PORTERBROOK |
| 47811 + | GL | P | IWLA | LE | |
| 47812 + | V | P | DFLH | FD | |
| 47813 + | GL | P | IWLA | LE | S.S. Great Britain |
| 47815 + | GL | P | IWLA | LE | Abertawe Landore |
| 47816 + | GL | P | ATLO | WN | |
| 47818 + | V | CD | CREL | MM | Springburn |
| 47826 + | I | P | ATLO | WN | Severn Valley Railway |
| 47828 + | V | P | ATLO | WN | Kidderminster Bewdley Bridgnorth |
| 47829 + | 0 | P | DFLH | FD | |
| 47830 + | GL | P | ATLO | WN | |
| 47832 + | GL | P | IWLA | LE | |
| 47839 + | RV | RV | RTLO | CP | |
| 47840 + | B | P | ATLO | WN | NORTH STAR |
| 47841 + | V | P | ATLO | WN | Spirit of Chester |
| 47843 + | V | P | DFLH | FD | VULCAN |
| 47844 | V | P | SBXL | ZC | |
| 47847 + | BL | P | DFLH | FD | Railway World Magazine/Brian Morrison |
| 47848 + | V | P | DFLH | FD | Newton Abbot Festival of Transport |
| 47851 + | GG | P | ATLO | WN | Traction Magazine |
| 47853 + | 0 | RV | RTLO | CP | RAIL EXPRESS |
| 47854 + | 0 | WC | MBDL | CS | |
| 47972 | 0 | FR | SDXL | CS | |

# CLASS 50 ENGLISH ELECTRIC Co-Co

**Built:** 1967–1968 by English Electric at Vulcan Foundry, Newton-le-Willows.
**Engine:** English Electric 16CVST of 2010 kW (2700 h.p.) at 850 r.p.m.
**Main Generator:** English Electric 840/4B.
**Traction Motors:** English Electric 538/5A.
**Maximum Tractive Effort:** 216 kN (48500 lbf).
**Continuous Tractive Effort:** 147 kN (33000 lbf) at 23.5 m.p.h.

| | |
|---|---|
| **Power At Rail:** 1540 kW (2070 h.p.). | **Train Brakes:** Air & vacuum. |
| **Brake Force:** 59 t. | **Dimensions:** 20.88 x 2.78 m. |
| **Weight:** 116.9 t. | **Wheel Diameter:** 1092 mm. |

**Design Speed:** 105 m.p.h.  
**Fuel Capacity:** 4796 litres.  
**Train Supply:** Electric, index 66.  

**Maximum Speed:** 90 (* 100) m.p.h.  
**RA:** 6.  
**Multiple Working:** Orange Square.  

Originally numbered D 416–49, 400.

**Non-standard livery/numbering:**

50017 "LMS Coronation Scot" style maroon with four gold bands.  
50044 Carries number D444.

| | | | | | |
|---|---|---|---|---|---|
| 50017 | * 0 | JK | MBDL | TM | |
| 50031 | B | 50 | MBDL | KR | Hood |
| 50044 | GG | 50 | MBDL | OC | |
| 50049 | B | 50 | MBDL | KR | Defiance |
| 50050 | BL | HS | DNLL | TM | Fearless |

# CLASS 52      WESTERN      C-C

**Built:** 1961–1964.  
**Engine:** Two Maybach MD655 of 1007 kW (1350 h.p) at 1500 r.p.m.  
**Transmission:** Hydraulic. Voith L630rV.  
**Maximum Tractive Effort:** 297 kN (66700 lbf).  
**Continuous Tractive Effort:** 201 kN (45200 lbf) at 14.5 m.p.h.  
**Power At Rail:** 1490 kW (2000 h.p.).    **Train Brakes:** Air & vacuum.  
**Brake Force:** 65 t.    **Dimensions:** 20.7 m x 2.78 m.  
**Weight:** 111 t.    **Wheel Diameter:** 1092 mm.  
**Design Speed:** 90 m.p.h.    **Maximum Speed:** 90 m.p.h.  
**Fuel Capacity:** 3900 litres.    **RA:** 7.  
**Train Supply:** Steam.    **Multiple Working:** Not equipped.  

**Non-standard livery:** Golden ochre.

Never allocated a TOPS number.

| | | | | | |
|---|---|---|---|---|---|
| D1015 | 0 | DT | MBDL | OC | SIR MISHA BLACK |

# CLASS 55     ENGLISH ELECTRIC     Co-Co

**Built:** 1961 by English Electric at Vulcan Foundry, Newton-le-Willows.  
**Engine:** Two Napier-Deltic D18-25 of 1230 kW (1650 h.p.) each at 1500 r.p.m.  
**Main Generators:** Two English Electric 829.  
**Traction Motors:** English Electric 538/A.  
**Maximum Tractive Effort:** 222 kN (50000 lbf).  
**Continuous Tractive Effort:** 136 kN (30500 lbf) at 32.5 m.p.h.  
**Power At Rail:** 1969 kW (2640 h.p.).    **Train Brakes:** Air & vacuum.  
**Brake Force:** 51 t.    **Dimensions:** 21.18 x 2.68 m.  
**Weight:** 104.7 t.    **Wheel Diameter:** 1092 mm.  
**Design Speed:** 105 m.p.h.    **Maximum Speed:** 100 m.p.h.  
**Fuel Capacity:** 3755 litres.    **RA:** 5.  
**Train Supply:** Electric, index 66.    **Multiple Working:** Not equipped.  

Originally numbered D 9009–19, 9000.

**Non-standard numbering:**

55009 Carries number D9009.
55016 Carries number 9016.
55022 Carries number D9000.

| 55009 | GG | DP | MBDL | BH | ALYCIDON |
|-------|----|----|------|----|----------|
| 55016 | G  | 90 | DNLL | CP | GORDON HIGHLANDER |
| 55019 | B  | DP | MBDL | BH | ROYAL HIGHLAND FUSILIER |
| 55022 | GG | 90 | DNLL | TM | ROYAL SCOTS GREY |

# CLASS 56      BRUSH/BR/PAXMAN      Co-Co

**Built:** 1976–1984 by Electroputere at Craiova, Romania (as sub contractors for Brush) or BREL at Doncaster or Crewe Works.
**Engine:** Ruston Paxman 16RK3CT of 2460 kW (3250 h.p.) at 900 r.p.m.
**Main Alternator:** Brush BA1101A.
**Traction Motors:** Brush TM73-62.
**Maximum Tractive Effort:** 275 kN (61800 lbf).
**Continuous Tractive Effort:** 240 kN (53950 lbf) at 16.8 m.p.h.
**Power At Rail:** 1790 kW (2400 h.p.).     **Train Brakes:** Air.
**Brake Force:** 60 t.                       **Dimensions:** 19.36 x 2.79 m.
**Weight:** 125.2 t.                         **Wheel Diameter:** 1143 mm.
**Design Speed:** 80 m.p.h.                  **Maximum Speed:** 80 m.p.h.
**Fuel Capacity:** 5228 litres.              **RA:** 7.
**Train Supply:** Not equipped.              **Multiple Working:** Red Diamond.

**Notes:** All equipped with Slow Speed Control.
56110 Carries its name on one side only.

**Non-standard liveries:**

56019 is as **FO** but with a red solebar stripe.
56063 is as **F**, but with the light grey replaced by a darker grey.
56027 and 56109 are **LH** but with the Loadhaul branding on one side only.

| 56003 | LH | E | WNZX | TT |
|-------|----|---|------|-----|
| 56004 | B  | E | WNYX | SP |
| 56006 | B  | E | WGAI | IM |
| 56007 | F  | E | WGAT | TE |
| 56010 | F  | E | WNZX | DR |
| 56011 | E  | E | WNXX | IM |
| 56018 | E  | E | WGAT | TE |
| 56019 | O  | X | WNSO | IM |
| 56021 | LH | E | WNXX | IM |
| 56022 | F  | X | WNSO | IM |
| 56025 | F  | E | WNXX | IM |
| 56027 | LH | E | WNTR | IM |
| 56029 | F  | E | WNYX | SP |
| 56031 | CE | E | WNSS | IM |
| 56032 | E  | E | WGAI | IM |
| 56033 | F  | E | WNSS | IM |
| 56034 | LH | E | WNYX | SP |
| 56036 | CE | E | WNYX | SP |

56033 Shotton Paper Mill

| 56037 | E | E | WNSS | IM | |
| 56038 | E | E | WGAT | TE | PATHFINDER TOURS 30 YEARS OF RAILTOURING 1973–2003 |
| 56039 | LH | E | WNZX | TE | |
| 56040 | F | E | WNXX | IM | |
| 56041 | E | E | WNSS | IM | |
| 56043 | F | E | WNXX | IM | |
| 56044 | F | E | WNYX | IM | |
| 56045 | LH | E | WNYX | IM | British Steel Shelton |
| 56046 | CE | E | WNSS | IM | |
| 56047 | CE | X | WNSO | IM | |
| 56048 | CE | E | WNSS | IM | |
| 56049 | CE | E | WGAT | TE | |
| 56050 | LH | E | WNYX | TO | British Steel Teesside |
| 56051 | E | E | WGAT | TE | |
| 56052 | F | E | WNXX | IM | |
| 56053 | F | E | WNXX | DR | |
| 56054 | F | E | WGAT | TE | British Steel Llanwern |
| 56055 | LH | E | WNTR | DR | |
| 56056 | F | E | WGAT | TE | |
| 56057 | E | E | WNYX | IM | British Fuels |
| 56058 | E | E | WGAT | TE | |
| 56059 | E | E | WGAT | TE | |
| 56060 | E | E | WGAT | TE | |
| 56061 | F | E | WNYX | TT | |
| 56062 | E | E | WGAI | IM | |
| 56063 | O | E | WNSS | IM | |
| 56064 | F | E | WNXX | IM | |
| 56065 | E | E | WGAT | TE | |
| 56066 | F | E | WNZX | SP | |
| 56067 | E | E | WGAT | TE | |
| 56068 | E | E | WNTR | IM | |
| 56069 | E | E | WGAI | IM | Wolverhampton Steel Terminal |
| 56070 | F | E | WGAT | TE | |
| 56071 | E | E | WGAT | TE | |
| 56072 | F | E | WGAI | IM | |
| 56073 | F | E | WNSS | IM | Tremorfa Steelworks |
| 56074 | LH | E | WNXX | IM | |
| 56075 | F | E | WNYX | TT | |
| 56076 | F | E | WNXX | IM | |
| 56077 | LH | E | WNSS | CD | |
| 56078 | BL | E | WGAI | IM | Doncaster Enterprise |
| 56079 | F | E | WNXX | IM | |
| 56081 | E | E | WGAI | IM | |
| 56082 | F | E | WNXX | IM | |
| 56083 | LH | E | WGAT | TE | |
| 56084 | LH | E | WNXX | IM | |
| 56085 | LH | E | WNXX | TE | |
| 56086 | F | E | WNXX | IM | The Magistrates' Association |
| 56087 | E | E | WGAI | IM | ABP Port of Hull |
| 56088 | E | E | WGAI | IM | |

| | | | | | |
|---|---|---|---|---|---|
| 56089 | E | E | WNXX | IM | |
| 56090 | LH | E | WGAI | IM | |
| 56091 | E | E | WGAI | IM | Stanton |
| 56093 | F | E | WNXX | DR | |
| 56094 | E | E | WNTR | TE | Eggborough Power Station |
| 56095 | E | E | WGAT | TE | |
| 56096 | E | E | WGAI | IM | |
| 56098 | F | E | WNSS | IM | |
| 56099 | F | E | WGAI | IM | |
| 56100 | LH | E | WGAI | TE | |
| 56101 | F | E | WNXX | IM | Mutual Improvement |
| 56102 | LH | E | WNTR | TE | |
| 56103 | E | E | WGAI | IM | STORA |
| 56104 | F | E | WGAI | IM | |
| 56105 | E | E | WNTR | IM | |
| 56106 | LH | E | WGAT | TE | |
| 56107 | LH | E | WGAI | IM | |
| 56108 | F | E | WNXX | TE | |
| 56109 | LH | E | WGAI | IM | |
| 56110 | LH | E | WNSS | IM | Croft |
| 56111 | LH | E | WNTR | TE | |
| 56112 | LH | E | WNTR | IM | Stainless Pioneer |
| 56113 | E | E | WGAI | IM | |
| 56114 | E | E | WGAI | IM | |
| 56115 | E | E | WGAI | IM | Barry Needham |
| 56116 | LH | E | WNSS | IM | |
| 56117 | E | E | WGAT | TE | |
| 56118 | LH | E | WGAI | IM | |
| 56119 | E | E | WGAT | TE | |
| 56120 | E | E | WGAI | IM | |
| 56121 | F | E | WNYX | SP | |
| 56124 | F | E | WNYX | KY | |
| 56125 | F | X | WNSO | IM | |
| 56127 | F | E | WNXX | TE | |
| 56128 | F | E | WNXX | IM | |
| 56129 | F | E | WNTR | TE | |
| 56130 | LH | E | WNXX | TI | |
| 56131 | F | E | WNSS | IM | Ellington Colliery |
| 56132 | F | E | WNYX | SP | |
| 56133 | F | E | WGAT | TE | |
| 56134 | F | E | WNSS | IM | Blyth Power |

## CLASS 57                    BRUSH/GM                    Co-Co

**Built:** 1964–1965 by Brush Traction at Loughborough or BR at Crewe Works as Class 47. Rebuilt 1997–2004 by Brush Traction at Loughborough. 57301–57316 for Virgin Trains. 57602–57605 undergoing conversion for First Great Western.
**Engine:** General Motors 645-12E3 of 1860 kW (2500 h.p.) at 900 r.p.m.
**Main Alternator:** Brush BA1101A.
**Traction Motors:** Brush TM68-46.

**Maximum Tractive Effort:** 244.5 kN (55000 lbf).
**Continuous Tractive Effort:** 140 kN (31500 lbf) at ?? m.p.h.
**Power at Rail:** 1507 kW (2025 h.p.).    **Train Brakes:** Air.
**Brake Force:** 80 t.    **Dimensions:** 19.38 x 2.79 m.
**Weight:** 120.6 t.    **Wheel Diameter:** 1143 mm.
**Design Speed:** 75 m.p.h.    **Maximum Speed:** 75 m.p.h.
**Fuel Capacity:** 5550 litres.    **RA:** 6
**Train Supply:** Not equipped.    **Multiple Working:** Not equipped.

**Class 57/0. No Train Supply Equipment.**

| | | | | | |
|---|---|---|---|---|---|
| 57001 | (47356) | FL | P | DFTZ | FD | Freightliner Pioneer |
| 57002 | (47322) | FL | P | DFTZ | FD | Freightliner Phoenix |
| 57003 | (47317) | FL | P | DFTZ | FD | Freightliner Evolution |
| 57004 | (47347) | FL | P | DFTZ | FD | Freightliner Quality |
| 57005 | (47350) | FL | P | DFTZ | FD | Freightliner Excellence |
| 57006 | (47187) | FL | P | DFTZ | FD | Freightliner Reliance |
| 57007 | (47332) | FL | P | DFTZ | FD | Freightliner Bond |
| 57008 | (47060) | FL | P | DFTZ | FD | Freightliner Explorer |
| 57009 | (47079) | FL | P | DFTZ | FD | Freightliner Venturer |
| 57010 | (47231) | FL | P | DFTZ | FD | Freightliner Crusader |
| 57011 | (47329) | FL | P | DFTZ | FD | Freightliner Challenger |
| 57012 | (47204) | FL | P | DFTZ | FD | Freightliner Envoy |

**Class 57/3. Electric Train Supply Equipment.** Details as Class 57/0 except.

**Engine:** General Motors 645-F3B-12 Cylinder of 2050 kW (2750 h.p.).
**Fuel Capacity:** 5887 litres.    **Train Supply:** Electric, index 100.
**Design Speed:** 95 m.p.h.    **Maximum Speed:** 95 m.p.h.
**Brake Force:** 60 t.    **Weight:** 117 t.

| | | | | | | |
|---|---|---|---|---|---|---|
| 57301 | (47845) | d | **VT** | P | ATLO | WN | SCOTT TRACY |
| 57302 | (47827) | d | **VT** | P | ATLO | WN | VIRGIL TRACY |
| 57303 | (47705) | | **VT** | P | ATLO | WN | ALAN TRACY |
| 57304 | (47807) | | **VT** | P | ATLO | WN | GORDON TRACY |
| 57305 | (47822) | | **VT** | P | ATLO | WN | JOHN TRACY |
| 57306 | (47814) | | **VT** | P | ATLO | WN | JEFF TRACY |
| 57307 | (47225) | | **VT** | P | ATLO | WN | LADY PENELOPE |
| 57308 | (47846) | | **VT** | P | ATLO | WN | TIN TIN |
| 57309 | (47806) | | **VT** | P | ATLO | WN | BRAINS |
| 57310 | (47831) | d | **VT** | P | ATLO | WN | KYRANO |
| 57311 | (47817) | | **VT** | P | ATLO | WN | PARKER |
| 57312 | (47330) | | **VT** | P | ATLO | WN | THE HOOD |
| 57313 | (47    ) | | **VT** | P | | | |
| 57314 | (47    ) | | **VT** | P | | | |
| 57315 | (47    ) | | **VT** | P | | | |
| 57316 | (47    ) | | **VT** | P | | | |

**Class 57/6. Electric Train Supply Equipment.** Prototype loco (built 2001).

**Fuel Capacity:** 5887 litres.    **Train Supply:** Electric, index 95.
**Design Speed:** 95 m.p.h.    **Maximum Speed:** 95 m.p.h.

| | | | | | | |
|---|---|---|---|---|---|---|
| 57601 | (47825) | **P** | WC | IWLA | LE | |

**Class 57/6. Electric Train Supply Equipment.** Undergoing conversion. Details as Class 57/3.

| | | | | |
|---|---|---|---|---|
| 57602 (47337) | **GL** | P | IWLA | LE |
| 57603 (47349) | **GL** | P | IWLA | LE |
| 57604 (47209) | **GL** | P | | |
| 57605 (47206) | **GL** | P | | |

# CLASS 58          BREL/PAXMAN          Co-Co

**Built:** 1983–1987 by BREL at Doncaster Works.
**Engine:** Ruston Paxman 12RK3ACT of 2460 kW (3300 h.p.) at 1000 r.p.m.
**Main Alternator:** Brush BA1101B.          **Traction Motors:** Brush TM73-62.
**Maximum Tractive Effort:** 275 kN (61800 lbf).
**Continuous Tractive Effort:** 240 kN (53950 lbf) at 17.4 m.p.h.
**Power At Rail:** 1780 kW (2387 h.p.).          **Train Brakes:** Air.
**Brake Force:** 62 t.          **Dimensions:** 19.13 x 2.72 m.
**Weight:** 130 t.          **Wheel Diameter:** 1120 mm.
**Design Speed:** 80 m.p.h.          **Maximum Speed:** 80 m.p.h.
**Fuel Capacity:** 4214 litres.          **RA:** 7.
**Train Supply:** Not equipped.          **Multiple Working:** Red Diamond.

**Notes:** All equipped with Slow Speed Control.
58041 and 58043 are on hire to GIF, Spain.
58039 and 58044 are on long-term hire to ACTS, Netherlands and carry numbers 5811 (58039) and 5812 (58044). Other locos in the WFGA pool are due to follow in 2004.
Locos in the WFGF pool are the subject of a separate hire contract.

**Non-standard livery:**

58001 As **F0** but with a red solebar stripe..

| | | | | | |
|---|---|---|---|---|---|
| 58001 | **0** | E | WNXX | BH | |
| 58002 | **ML** | E | WNXX | EH | Daw Mill Colliery |
| 58003 | **F** | E | WNXX | TO | Markham Colliery |
| 58004 | **F** | E | WFGF | HM | |
| 58005 | **ML** | E | WFGF | LR | |
| 58006 | **F** | E | WFGF | HM | |
| 58007 | **F** | E | WFGF | HM | |
| 58008 | **ML** | E | WNXX | TT | |
| 58009 | **F** | E | WNXX | EH | |
| 58010 | **F** | E | WFGF | HM | |
| 58011 | **F** | E | WFGF | HM | |
| 58012 | **F** | E | WFGF | HM | |
| 58013 | **ML** | E | WFGF | EH | |
| 58014 | **ML** | E | WNXX | TT | |
| 58015 | **F** | E | WNXX | DR | |
| 58016 | **E** | E | WNXX | EH | |
| 58017 | **F** | E | WFGF | DR | |
| 58018 | **F** | E | WFGF | HM | |
| 58019 | **F** | E | WNXX | TO | Shirebrook Colliery |
| 58020 | **F** | E | WFGF | OC | Doncaster Works |

| | | | | | |
|---|---|---|---|---|---|
| 58021 | **ML** | E | WNXX | EH | Hither Green Depot |
| 58022 | **F** | E | WNXX | CD | |
| 58023 | **ML** | E | WNXX | TT | |
| 58024 | **E** | E | WFGF | OC | |
| 58025 | **F** | E | WFGF | EH | |
| 58026 | **F** | E | WNXX | EH | |
| 58027 | **F** | E | WFGF | HM | |
| 58028 | **F** | E | WNXX | TT | |
| 58029 | **F** | E | WFGF | EH | |
| 58030 | **E** | E | WFGF | EH | |
| 58031 | **F** | E | WNXX | EH | |
| 58032 | **ML** | E | WNXX | HM | |
| 58033 | **E** | E | WNXX | OC | |
| 58034 | **F** | E | WNXX | DR | |
| 58035 | **F** | E | WNXX | HM | |
| 58036 | **ML** | E | WFGA | TT | |
| 58037 | **E** | E | WNXX | EH | |
| 58038 | **ML** | E | WFGA | TT | |
| 58039 | **AC** | E | WFGA | TB | |
| 58040 | **F** | E | WNXX | HM | |
| 58041 | **GIF** | E | WKGS | ES | |
| 58042 | **ML** | E | WNXX | EH | |
| 58043 | **GIF** | E | WKGS | ES | |
| 58044 | **AC** | E | WFGA | TB | |
| 58045 | **F** | E | WNXX | OC | |
| 58046 | **ML** | E | WFGA | TO | |
| 58047 | **E** | E | WNXX | OC | |
| 58048 | **E** | E | WNXX | TT | |
| 58049 | **E** | E | WNXX | EH | |
| 58050 | **E** | E | WNXX | EH | Toton Traction Depot |

# CLASS 59　　　　GENERAL MOTORS　　　Co-Co

**Built:** 1985 (59001/59002/59004) or 1989 (59005) by General Motors, La Grange, Illinois, USA or 1990 (59101–5914), 1994 (59201) and 1995 (59202–59206) by General Motors, London, Ontario, Canada.
**Engine:** General Motors 645E3C two stroke of 2460 kW (3300 h.p.) at 900 r.p.m.
**Main Alternator:** General Motors AR11 MLD-D14A.
**Traction Motors:** General Motors D77B.
**Maximum Tractive Effort:** 506 kN (113 550 lbf).
**Continuous Tractive Effort:** 291 kN (65 300 lbf) at 14.3 m.p.h.
**Power At Rail:** 1889 kW (2533 h.p.).　　**Train Brakes:** Air.
**Brake Force:** 69 t.　　　　　　　　　　**Dimensions:** 21.35 x 2.65 m.
**Weight:** 121 t.　　　　　　　　　　　　**Wheel Diameter:** 1067 mm.
**Design Speed:** 60 (* 75) m.p.h.　　　　**Maximum Speed:** 60 (* 75) m.p.h.
**Fuel Capacity:** 4546 litres.　　　　　　**RA:** 7.
**Train Supply:** Not equipped.　　　　　**Multiple Working:** AAR System.

**Class 59/0. Owned by Foster-Yeoman.**

| | | | | | |
|---|---|---|---|---|---|
| 59001 | **FY** | FY | XYPO | MD | YEOMAN ENDEAVOUR |
| 59002 | **MR** | FY | XYPO | MD | ALAN J DAY |

| 59004 | **YO** | FY | XYPO | MD | PAUL A HAMMOND |
| 59005 | **FY** | FY | XYPO | MD | KENNETH J PAINTER |

**Class 59/1. Owned by Hanson Quarry Products.**

| 59101 | **HA** | HA | XYPA | MD | Village of Whatley |
| 59102 | **HA** | HA | XYPA | MD | Village of Chantry |
| 59103 | **HA** | HA | XYPA | MD | Village of Mells |
| 59104 | **HA** | HA | XYPA | MD | Village of Great Elm |

**Class 59/2. Owned by EWS.**

| 59201 * | **E** | E | WDAG | HG | Vale of York |
| 59202 * | **E** | E | WDAG | HG | Vale of White Horse |
| 59203 * | **E** | E | WDAG | HG | Vale of Pickering |
| 59204 * | **E** | E | WDAG | HG | Vale of Glamorgan |
| 59205 b* | **E** | E | WDAG | HG | L. Keith McNair |
| 59206 b* | **E** | E | WDAG | HG | Pride of Ferrybridge |

# CLASS 60        BRUSH/MIRRLEES        Co-Co

**Built:** 1989–1993 by Brush Traction at Loughborough.
**Engine:** Mirrlees 8MB275T of 2310 kW (3100 h.p.) at 1000 r.p.m.
**Main Alternator:** Brush BA1000.        **Traction Motors:** Brush TM216.
**Maximum Tractive Effort:** 500 kN (106500 lbf).
**Continuous Tractive Effort:** 336 kN (71570 lbf) at 17.4 m.p.h.
**Power At Rail:** 1800 kW (2415 h.p.).        **Train Brakes:** Air.
**Brake Force:** 74 (+ 62) t.        **Dimensions:** 21.34 x 2.64 m.
**Weight:** 129 (+ 131) t.        **Wheel Diameter:** 1118 mm.
**Design Speed:** 62 m.p.h.        **Maximum Speed:** 60 m.p.h.
**Fuel Capacity:** 4546 (+ 5225) litres.        **RA:** 7.
**Train Supply:** Not equipped.        **Multiple Working:** Within class.

**Notes:** All equipped with Slow Speed Control.
60034, 60038, 60061, 60064, 60066, 60072, 60073, 60077, 60079, 60082,
60084 and 60088 carry their names on one side only.

| 60001 | **E** | E | WCAT | TE | The Railway Observer |
| 60002 + | **E** | E | WCAT | TE | High Peak |
| 60003 + | **E** | E | WCAK | CF | FREIGHT TRANSPORT ASSOCIATION |
| 60004 + | **E** | E | WCAK | CF | |
| 60005 + | **E** | E | WCAK | CF | BP Gas Avonmouth |
| 60006 | **CU** | E | WCAT | TE | Scunthorpe Ironmaster |
| 60007 + | **LH** | E | WCAI | IM | |
| 60008 | **LH** | E | WCAT | TE | GYPSUM QUEEN II |
| 60009 + | **E** | E | WCAI | IM | |
| 60010 + | **E** | E | WCAK | CF | |
| 60011 | **ML** | E | WCAT | TE | |
| 60012 + | **E** | E | WCAI | IM | |
| 60013 | **F** | E | WCAT | TE | Robert Boyle |
| 60014 | **F** | E | WCAT | TE | Alexander Fleming |
| 60015 + | **F** | E | WCAK | CF | Bow Fell |
| 60016 | **E** | E | WCAN | TO | RAIL Magazine |
| 60017 + | **E** | E | WCAT | TE | Shotton Works Centenary Year 1996 |

| | | | | | |
|---|---|---|---|---|---|
| 60018 | | E | E | WCAT | TE |
| 60019 | | E | E | WCAN | TO |
| 60020 + | | E | E | WCAI | IM |
| 60021 + | | E | E | WCAI | IM |
| 60022 + | | E | E | WCAI | IM |
| 60023 + | | E | E | WCAI | IM |
| 60024 + | | E | E | WCAN | TO |
| 60025 + | | E | E | WCAI | IM | Caledonian Paper |
| 60026 + | | E | E | WCAK | CF |
| 60027 + | | E | E | WCAI | IM | John Flamsteed |
| 60028 + | | F | E | WCAI | IM | Clitheroe Castle |
| 60029 | | E | E | WCAN | TO |
| 60030 + | | E | E | WCAK | CF | ABP Connect |
| 60031 | | E | E | WCAN | TO | William Booth |
| 60032 | | F | E | WCAN | TO | Tees Steel Express |
| 60033 + | CU | E | WCAT | TE | Carnedd Llewelyn |
| 60034 | | F | E | WCAN | TO |
| 60035 | | E | E | WCAT | TE | GEFCO |
| 60036 | | E | E | WCAN | TO | Aberddawan/Aberthaw |
| 60037 + | | E | E | WCAK | CF | AvestaPolarit |
| 60038 + | | E | E | WCAI | IM |
| 60039 | | E | E | WCAT | TE |
| 60040 | | E | E | WCAT | TE |
| 60041 + | | E | E | WCAK | CF | The Hundred of Hoo |
| 60042 + | | E | E | WCAT | TE |
| 60043 | | E | E | WCAT | TE |
| 60044 | ML | E | WCAT | TE | The Permanent Way Institution |
| 60045 | | E | E | WCAT | TE | William Wilberforce |
| 60046 + | | F | E | WCAN | TO |
| 60047 + | | E | E | WCAN | TO | EASTERN |
| 60048 | | E | E | WCAT | TE |
| 60049 + | | E | E | WCAT | TE |
| 60050 + | | E | E | WCAT | TE |
| 60051 + | | E | E | WCAK | CF |
| 60052 + | | E | E | WCAK | CF | Glofa Twr – The last deep mine in Wales – Tower Colliery |
| 60053 + | | E | E | WCAT | TE | NORDIC TERMINAL |
| 60054 + | | F | E | WCAN | TO | Charles Babbage |
| 60055 + | | F | E | WCAI | IM | Thomas Barnardo |
| 60056 + | | F | E | WCAK | CF | William Beveridge |
| 60057 | | F | E | WCAN | TO | Adam Smith |
| 60058 + | | E | E | WCAI | IM |
| 60059 + | LH | E | WCAK | CF | Swinden Dalesman |
| 60060 | | F | E | WCAT | TE | James Watt |
| 60061 | | F | E | WCAT | TE | Alexander Graham Bell |
| 60062 | | F | E | WCAT | TE | Samuel Johnson |
| 60063 | | F | E | WCAT | TE | James Murray |
| 60064 + | | F | E | WCAK | CF | Back Tor |
| 60065 | | E | E | WCAT | TE | Spirit of JAGUAR |
| 60066 | | F | E | WCAN | TO | John Logie Baird |
| 60067 + | | F | E | WCAN | TO | James Clerk-Maxwell |

| 60068 | F | E | WCAN | TO | Charles Darwin |
| 60069 | F | E | WCAN | TO | Humphry Davy |
| 60070 + | F | E | WCAK | CF | John Loudon McAdam |
| 60071 + | E | E | WCAN | TO | |
| 60072 | F | E | WCAN | TO | Cairn Toul |
| 60073 | F | E | WCAT | TE | Cairn Gorm |
| 60074 | F | E | WCAT | TE | |
| 60075 | E | E | WCAN | TO | |
| 60076 | F | E | WCAN | TO | |
| 60077 + | E | E | WCAK | CF | Canisp |
| 60078 | ML | E | WCAT | TE | |
| 60079 | F | E | WCAT | TE | Foinaven |
| 60080 + | E | E | WCAI | IM | Little Eaton Primary School Little |
| | | | | | Eaton Railsafe Trophy Winners 2002 |
| 60081 + | GW | E | WCAK | CF | ISAMBARD KINGDOM BRUNEL |
| 60082 | F | E | WCAT | TE | Mam Tor |
| 60083 | E | E | WCAT | TE | Mountsorrel |
| 60084 | F | E | WCAN | TO | Cross Fell |
| 60085 | E | E | WCAT | TE | MINI Pride of Oxford |
| 60086 | F | E | WCAT | TE | Schiehallion |
| 60087 | F | E | WCAN | TO | Slioch |
| 60088 | F | E | WCAT | TE | Buachaille Etive Mor |
| 60089 + | E | E | WCAK | CF | THE RAILWAY HORSE |
| 60090 + | E | E | WCAI | IM | Quinag |
| 60091 + | F | E | WCAK | CF | An Teallach |
| 60092 | F | E | WCAT | TE | Reginald Munns |
| 60093 | E | E | WCAT | TE | |
| 60094 | F | E | WCAN | TO | Tryfan |
| 60095 | F | E | WCAN | TO | |
| 60096 + | E | E | WCAK | CF | |
| 60097 + | E | E | WCAI | IM | ABP Port of Grimsby & Immingham |
| 60098 + | F | E | WCAK | CF | Charles Francis Brush |
| 60099 | F | E | WCAT | TE | Ben More Assynt |
| 60100 | E | E | WCAN | TO | Pride of Acton |

## CLASS 66          GENERAL MOTORS          Co-Co

**Built:** 1998–2004 by General Motors, London, Ontario, Canada (Model JT42CWR).
**Engine:** General Motors 12N-710G3B-EC two stroke of 2385 kW (3200 h.p.) at 900 r.p.m.
**Main Alternator:** General Motors AR8/C86.
**Traction Motors:** General Motors D43TR.
**Maximum Tractive Effort:** 409 kN (92000 lbf).
**Continuous Tractive Effort:** 260 kN (58390 lbf) at 15.9 m.p.h.
**Power At Rail:** 1850 kW (2480 h.p.).     **Train Brakes:** Air.
**Brake Force:** 68 t.                      **Dimensions:** 21.35 x 2.64 m.
**Weight:** 126 t.                          **Wheel Diameter:** 1120 mm.
**Design Speed:** 87.5 m.p.h.               **Maximum Speed:** 75 m.p.h.
**Fuel Capacity:** 6550 litres.             **RA:** 7.
**Train Supply:** Not equipped.        ·    **Multiple Working:** AAR System.

**Notes:** All equipped with Slow Speed Control.
Locos in pool WBBM are fitted with RETB to allow working on the West Highland and Far North Lines.

### Class 66/0. EWS-operated locomotives.

| | | | | | | | | | | |
|---|---|---|---|---|---|---|---|---|---|---|
| 66001 | | E | A | WBAT | TE | 66047 | k | E | A | WBAT | TE |
| 66002 | | E | A | WBAN | TO | 66048 | k | E | A | WBAI | IM |
| 66003 | k | E | A | WBAT | TE | 66049 | k | E | A | WBAM | ML |
| 66004 | k | E | A | WBAN | TO | 66050 | k | E | A | WBAI | IM |
| 66005 | k | E | A | WBAI | IM | 66051 | k | E | A | WBAT | TE |
| 66006 | k | E | A | WBAT | TE | 66052 | k | E | A | WBAI | IM |
| 66007 | k | E | A | WBAI | IM | 66053 | k | E | A | WBAI | IM |
| 66008 | k | E | A | WBAK | CF | 66054 | k | E | A | WBAK | CF |
| 66009 | k | E | A | WBAH | EH | 66055 | k | E | A | WBAN | TO |
| 66010 | k | E | A | WBAI | IM | 66056 | k | E | A | WBAN | TO |
| 66011 | k | E | A | WBAI | IM | 66057 | k | E | A | WBAN | TO |
| 66012 | k | E | A | WBAI | IM | 66058 | k | E | A | WBAN | TO |
| 66013 | k | E | A | WBAH | EH | 66059 | k | E | A | WBAN | TO |
| 66014 | k | E | A | WBAI | IM | 66060 | k | E | A | WBAI | IM |
| 66015 | k | E | A | WBAH | EH | 66061 | k | E | A | WBAH | EH |
| 66016 | k | E | A | WBAH | EH | 66062 | k | E | A | WBAK | CF |
| 66017 | k | E | A | WBAN | TO | 66063 | k | E | A | WBAI | IM |
| 66018 | k | E | A | WBAI | IM | 66064 | k | E | A | WBAH | EH |
| 66019 | k | E | A | WBAK | CF | 66065 | k | E | A | WBAM | ML |
| 66020 | k | E | A | WBAT | TE | 66066 | k | E | A | WBAM | ML |
| 66021 | k | E | A | WBAK | CF | 66067 | k | E | A | WBAK | CF |
| 66022 | k | E | A | WBAN | TO | 66068 | k | E | A | WBAI | IM |
| 66023 | k | E | A | WBAI | IM | 66069 | k | E | A | WBAI | IM |
| 66024 | k | E | A | WBAN | TO | 66070 | k | E | A | WBAT | TE |
| 66025 | k | E | A | WBAK | CF | 66071 | k | E | A | WBAI | IM |
| 66026 | k | E | A | WBAI | IM | 66072 | k | E | A | WBAI | IM |
| 66027 | k | E | A | WBAI | IM | 66073 | k | E | A | WBAI | IM |
| 66028 | k | E | A | WBAM | ML | 66074 | k | E | A | WBAN | TO |
| 66029 | k | E | A | WBAK | CF | 66075 | k | E | A | WBAN | TO |
| 66030 | k | E | A | WBAT | TE | 66076 | k | E | A | WBAK | CF |
| 66031 | k | E | A | WBAK | CF | 66077 | k | E | A | WBAI | IM |
| 66032 | k | E | A | WBAK | CF | 66078 | k | E | A | WBAT | TE |
| 66033 | k | E | A | WBAH | EH | 66079 | k | E | A | WBAK | CF |
| 66034 | k | E | A | WBAH | EH | 66080 | k | E | A | WBAK | CF |
| 66035 | k | E | A | WBAM | ML | 66081 | k | E | A | WBAI | IM |
| 66036 | k | E | A | WBAI | IM | 66082 | | E | A | WBAH | EH |
| 66037 | k | E | A | WBAN | TO | 66083 | k | E | A | WBAT | TE |
| 66038 | k | E | A | WBAK | CF | 66084 | k | E | A | WBAI | IM |
| 66039 | k | E | A | WBAI | IM | 66085 | k | E | A | WBAI | IM |
| 66040 | k | E | A | WBAN | TO | 66086 | k | E | A | WBAN | TO |
| 66041 | k | E | A | WBAT | TE | 66087 | k | E | A | WBAN | TO |
| 66042 | k | E | A | WBAN | TO | 66088 | k | E | A | WBAK | CF |
| 66043 | k | E | A | WBAK | CF | 66089 | k | E | A | WBAT | TE |
| 66044 | k | E | A | WBAT | TE | 66090 | | E | A | WBAK | CF |
| 66045 | k | E | A | WBAI | IM | 66091 | k | E | A | WBAI | IM |
| 66046 | k | E | A | WBAI | IM | 66092 | k | E | A | WBAK | CF |

| | | | | | | | | | | | |
|---|---|---|---|---|---|---|---|---|---|---|---|
| 66093 | k | E | A | WBAT | TE | | 66144 | | E | A | WBAK | CF |

| Code | k | E | A | Station | Loc | Code | k | E | A | Station | Loc |
|---|---|---|---|---|---|---|---|---|---|---|---|
| 66093 | k | E | A | WBAT | TE | 66144 | | E | A | WBAK | CF |
| 66094 | k | E | A | WBAI | IM | 66145 | k | E | A | WBAK | CF |
| 66095 | k | E | A | WBBM | ML | 66146 | k | E | A | WBAH | EH |
| 66096 | k | E | A | WBBM | ML | 66147 | k | E | A | WBAI | IM |
| 66097 | k | E | A | WBBM | ML | 66148 | k | E | A | WBAN | TO |
| 66098 | k | E | A | WBBM | ML | 66149 | | E | A | WBAT | TE |
| 66099 | | E | A | WBBM | ML | 66150 | k | E | A | WBAN | TO |
| 66100 | | E | A | WBBM | ML | 66151 | k | E | A | WBAK | CF |
| 66101 | | E | A | WBBM | ML | 66152 | k | E | A | WBAM | ML |
| 66102 | | E | A | WBBM | ML | 66153 | k | E | A | WBAI | IM |
| 66103 | | E | A | WBBM | ML | 66154 | k | E | A | WBAI | IM |
| 66104 | k | E | A | WBBM | ML | 66155 | k | E | A | WBAI | IM |
| 66105 | k | E | A | WBBM | ML | 66156 | k | E | A | WBAT | TE |
| 66106 | k | E | A | WBBM | ML | 66157 | k | E | A | WBAK | CF |
| 66107 | | E | A | WBBM | ML | 66158 | k | E | A | WBAI | IM |
| 66108 | k | E | A | WBBM | ML | 66159 | k | E | A | WBAN | TO |
| 66109 | k | E | A | WBAM | ML | 66160 | k | E | A | WBAI | IM |
| 66110 | k | E | A | WBBM | ML | 66161 | k | E | A | WBAT | TE |
| 66111 | k | E | A | WBBM | ML | 66162 | k | E | A | WBAH | EH |
| 66112 | | E | A | WBBM | ML | 66163 | k | E | A | WBAN | TO |
| 66113 | | E | A | WBBM | ML | 66164 | k | E | A | WBAK | CF |
| 66114 | k | E | A | WBBM | ML | 66165 | k | E | A | WBAK | CF |
| 66115 | k | E | A | WBAK | CF | 66166 | k | E | A | WBAI | IM |
| 66116 | k | E | A | WBAM | ML | 66167 | k | E | A | WBAI | IM |
| 66117 | k | E | A | WBAN | TO | 66168 | k | E | A | WBAK | CF |
| 66118 | k | E | A | WBAT | TE | 66169 | k | E | A | WBAH | EH |
| 66119 | k | E | A | WBAN | TO | 66170 | k | E | A | WBAT | TE |
| 66120 | k | E | A | WBAI | IM | 66171 | k | E | A | WBAN | TO |
| 66121 | k | E | A | WBAI | IM | 66172 | k | E | A | WBAI | IM |
| 66122 | k | E | A | WBAH | EH | 66173 | k | E | A | WBAH | EH |
| 66123 | k | E | A | WBAI | IM | 66174 | k | E | A | WBAN | TO |
| 66124 | k | E | A | WBAI | IM | 66175 | k | E | A | WBAN | TO |
| 66125 | k | E | A | WBAT | TE | 66176 | k | E | A | WBAK | CF |
| 66126 | k | E | A | WBAN | TO | 66177 | k | E | A | WBAI | IM |
| 66127 | k | E | A | WBAK | CF | 66178 | k | E | A | WBAN | TO |
| 66128 | k | E | A | WBAI | IM | 66179 | k | E | A | WBAK | CF |
| 66129 | k | E | A | WBAN | TO | 66180 | k | E | A | WBAM | ML |
| 66130 | k | E | A | WBAI | IM | 66181 | k | E | A | WBAK | CF |
| 66131 | k | E | A | WBAI | IM | 66182 | k | E | A | WBAN | TO |
| 66132 | k | E | A | WBAH | EH | 66183 | k | E | A | WBAI | IM |
| 66133 | k | E | A | WBAM | ML | 66184 | k | E | A | WBAT | TE |
| 66134 | k | E | A | WBAI | IM | 66185 | k | E | A | WBAI | IM |
| 66135 | k | E | A | WBAK | CF | 66186 | k | E | A | WBAM | ML |
| 66136 | k | E | A | WBAM | ML | 66187 | k | E | A | WBAK | CF |
| 66137 | k | E | A | WBAI | IM | 66188 | k | E | A | WBAN | TO |
| 66138 | k | E | A | WBAT | TE | 66189 | k | E | A | WBAH | EH |
| 66139 | k | E | A | WBAI | IM | 66190 | k | E | A | WBAT | TE |
| 66140 | k | E | A | WBAT | TE | 66191 | k | E | A | WBAK | CF |
| 66141 | k | E | A | WBAI | IM | 66192 | k | E | A | WBAT | TE |
| 66142 | k | E | A | WBAN | TO | 66193 | k | E | A | WBAM | ML |
| 66143 | | E | A | WBAK | CF | 66194 | k | E | A | WBAN | TO |

| | | | | | | | | | | | |
|---|---|---|---|---|---|---|---|---|---|---|---|
| 66195 | k | E | A | WBAN | TO | | 66223 | k | E | A | WBAT | TE |
| 66196 | k | E | A | WBAN | TO | | 66224 | k | E | A | WBAT | TE |
| 66197 | k | E | A | WBAI | IM | | 66225 | k | E | A | WBAN | TO |
| 66198 | k | E | A | WBAT | TE | | 66226 | k | E | A | WBAI | IM |
| 66199 | k | E | A | WBAK | CF | | 66227 | k | E | A | WBAT | TE |
| 66200 | k | E | A | WBAM | ML | | 66228 | k | E | A | WBAI | IM |
| 66201 | k | E | A | WBAI | IM | | 66229 | k | E | A | WBAK | CF |
| 66202 | k | E | A | WBAK | CF | | 66230 | k | E | A | WBAI | IM |
| 66203 | k | E | A | WBAT | TE | | 66231 | k | E | A | WBAN | TO |
| 66204 | k | E | A | WBAI | IM | | 66232 | k | E | A | WBAN | TO |
| 66205 | k | E | A | WBAI | IM | | 66233 | k | E | A | WBAT | TE |
| 66206 | k | E | A | WBAK | CF | | 66234 | k | E | A | WBAI | IM |
| 66207 | k | E | A | WBAI | IM | | 66235 | k | E | A | WBAK | CF |
| 66208 | k | E | A | WBAN | TO | | 66236 | k | E | A | WBAK | CF |
| 66209 | k | E | A | WBAI | IM | | 66237 | k | E | A | WBAI | IM |
| 66210 | k | E | A | WBAN | TO | | 66238 | k | E | A | WBAH | EH |
| 66211 | k | E | A | WBAT | TE | | 66239 | k | E | A | WBAK | CF |
| 66212 | k | E | A | WBAK | CF | | 66240 | k | E | A | WBAI | IM |
| 66213 | k | E | A | WBAI | IM | | 66241 | k | E | A | WBAK | CF |
| 66214 | k | E | A | WBAK | CF | | 66242 | k | E | A | WBAI | IM |
| 66215 | k | E | A | WBAK | CF | | 66243 | k | E | A | WBAN | TO |
| 66216 | k | E | A | WBAH | EH | | 66244 | k | E | A | WBAT | TE |
| 66217 | k | E | A | WBAH | EH | | 66245 | k | E | A | WBAI | IM |
| 66218 | k | E | A | WBAN | TO | | 66246 | k | E | A | WBAN | TO |
| 66219 | k | E | A | WBAN | TO | | 66247 | k | E | A | WBAN | TO |
| 66220 | k | E | A | WBAI | IM | | 66248 | k | E | A | WBAM | ML |
| 66221 | k | E | A | WBAI | IM | | 66249 | k | E | A | WBAH | EH |
| 66222 | k | E | A | WBAK | CF | | 66250 | k | E | A | WBAK | CF |

## Names:

66002 Lafarge Quorn.
66022 Lafarge Charnwood.
66042 Lafarge Buddon Wood.

## Class 66/4. Direct Rail Services-operated locomotives.
Details as Class 66/0.

## Advertising livery:

66405 WH Malcolm (details awaited)

| | | | | |
|---|---|---|---|---|
| 66401 | **DS** | P | XHCK | KM |
| 66402 | **DS** | P | XHCK | KM |
| 66403 | **DS** | P | XHCK | KM |
| 66404 | **DS** | P | XHCK | KM |
| 66405 | **AL** | P | XHCK | KM |
| 66406 | **DS** | P | XHCK | KM |
| 66407 | **DS** | P | XHCK | KM |
| 66408 | **DS** | P | XHCK | KM |
| 66409 | **DS** | P | XHCK | KM |
| 66410 | **DS** | P | XHCK | KM |

**Class 66/5. Freightliner-operated locomotives.** Details as Class 66/0.

| | | | | | |
|---|---|---|---|---|---|
| 66501 | FL | P | DFGM | FD | Japan 2001 |
| 66502 | FL | P | DFGM | FD | Basford Hall Centenary 2001 |
| 66503 | FL | P | DFGM | FD | |
| 66504 | FL | P | DFGM | FD | |
| 66505 | FL | P | DFGM | FD | |
| 66506 | FL | H | DFRT | FD | Crewe Regeneration |
| 66507 | FL | H | DFRT | FD | |
| 66508 | FL | H | DFRT | FD | |
| 66509 | FL | H | DFRT | FD | |
| 66510 | FL | H | DFRT | FD | |
| 66511 | FL | H | DFRT | FD | |
| 66512 | FL | H | DFRT | FD | |
| 66513 | FL | H | DFRT | FD | |
| 66514 | FL | H | DFRT | FD | |
| 66515 | FL | H | DFRT | FD | |
| 66516 | FL | H | DFRT | FD | |
| 66517 | FL | H | DFRT | FD | |
| 66518 | FL | H | DFRT | FD | |
| 66519 | FL | H | DFRT | FD | |
| 66520 | FL | H | DFRT | FD | |
| 66521 | FL | H | SAXL | ZF | |
| 66522 | FL | H | DFHH | LD | |
| 66523 | FL | H | DFHH | FD | |
| 66524 | FL | H | DFHH | LD | |
| 66525 | FL | H | DFHH | FD | |
| 66526 | FL | P | DFHH | LD | Driver Steve Dunn (George) |
| 66527 | FL | P | DFHH | LD | Don Raider |
| 66528 | FL | P | DFHH | FD | |
| 66529 | FL | P | DFHH | FD | |
| 66530 | FL | P | DFHH | LD | |
| 66531 | FL | P | DFHH | FD | |
| 66532 | FL | P | DFGM | FD | P&O Nedlloyd Atlas |
| 66533 | FL | P | DFGM | FD | Hanjin Express/Senator Express |
| 66534 | FL | P | DFGM | FD | OOCL Express |
| 66535 | FL | P | DFGM | FD | |
| 66536 | FL | P | DFGM | FD | |
| 66537 | FL | P | DFGM | FD | |
| 66538 | FL | H | DFGM | FD | |
| 66539 | FL | H | DFGM | FD | |
| 66540 | FL | H | DFGM | FD | |
| 66541 | FL | H | DFGM | FD | |
| 66542 | FL | H | DFGM | FD | |
| 66543 | FL | H | DFGM | FD | |
| 66544 | FL | P | DFHH | LD | |
| 66545 | FL | P | DFHH | FD | |
| 66546 | FL | P | DFHH | FD | |
| 66547 | FL | P | DFHH | LD | |
| 66548 | FL | P | DFHH | LD | |
| 66549 | FL | P | DFHH | LD | |

| 66550 | **FL** | P | DFHH | LD |
| 66551 | **FL** | P | DFHH | LD |
| 66552 | **FL** | P | DFHH | LD |
| 66553 | **FL** | P | DFHH | LD |
| 66554 | **FL** | H | DFHH | LD |
| 66555 | **FL** | H | DFHH | LD |
| 66556 | **FL** | H | DFHH | LD |
| 66557 | **FL** | H | DFHH | FD |
| 66558 | **FL** | H | DFHH | FD |
| 66559 | **FL** | H | DFHH | LD |
| 66560 | **FL** | H | DFHH | FD |
| 66561 | **FL** | H | DFHH | FD |
| 66562 | **FL** | H | DFHH | LD |
| 66563 | **FL** | H | DFHH | FD |
| 66564 | **FL** | H | DFHH | LD |
| 66565 | **FL** | H | DFHH | LD |
| 66566 | **FL** | H | DFHH | LD |
| 66567 | **FL** | H | DFGM | FD |
| 66568 | **FL** | H | DFGM | FD |
| 66569 | **FL** | H | DFGM | FD |
| 66570 | **FL** | H | DFGM | FD |
| 66571 | **FL** | H | DFGM | FD |
| 66572 | **FL** | H | DFGM | FD |
| 66573 | **FL** | H | | |
| 66574 | **FL** | H | | |

**Class 66/6. Freightliner-operated locomotives with modified gear ratios.**
Details as Class 66/0 except:

**Maximum Tractive Effort:** 467 kN (105080 lbf).
**Continuous Tractive Effort:** 296 kN (66630 lbf) at 14.0 m.p.h.
**Design Speed:** 65 m.p.h.          **Maximum Speed:** 65 m.p.h.

| 66601 | **FL** | P | DFHH | FD | The Hope Valley |
| 66602 | **FL** | P | DFRT | FD | |
| 66603 | **FL** | P | DFRT | FD | |
| 66604 | **FL** | P | DFRT | FD | |
| 66605 | **FL** | P | DFRT | FD | |
| 66606 | **FL** | P | DFRT | FD | |
| 66607 | **FL** | P | DFHH | FD | |
| 66608 | **FL** | P | DFHH | FD | |
| 66609 | **FL** | P | DFHH | FD | |
| 66610 | **FL** | P | DFHH | FD | |
| 66611 | **FL** | P | DFHH | FD | |
| 66612 | **FL** | P | DFHH | FD | Forth Raider |

| 66613 | **FL** | H |
| 66614 | **FL** | H |
| 66615 | **FL** | H |
| 66616 | **FL** | H |
| 66617 | **FL** | H |
| 66618 | **FL** | H |

### Class 66/7. GB Railfreight-operated locomotives.
Details as Class 66/0.

**Notes:** 66716 and 66717 are currently on hire to Freightliner Heavy Haul.
GBRf also regularly hire their Class 66s to Freightliner (Intermodal) and DRS.

### Non Standard/Advertising liveries:

66705 **GB** livery but with the addition of "Union Jack" bodyside vinyls.
66709 Black and Orange with MEDITE branding.

| 66701 | **GB** | H | GBRT | WN | Railtrack National Logistics |
| 66702 | **GB** | H | GBRT | WN | Blue Lightning |
| 66703 | **GB** | H | GBRT | WN | Doncaster PSB 1981–2002 |
| 66704 | **GB** | H | GBRT | WN | Colchester Power Signalbox |
| 66705 | **GB** | H | GBRT | WN | Golden Jubilee |
| 66706 | **GB** | H | GBRT | WN | Nene Valley |
| 66707 | **GB** | H | GBRT | WN | Sir Sam Fay GREAT CENTRAL RAILWAY |
| 66708 | **GB** | H | GBCM | WN | |
| 66709 | **AL** | H | GBCM | WN | Joseph Arnold Davies |
| 66710 | **GB** | H | GBCM | WN | |
| 66711 | **GB** | H | GBCM | WN | |
| 66712 | **GB** | H | GBCM | WN | |
| 66713 | **GB** | H | GBCM | WN | Forest City |
| 66714 | **GB** | H | GBCM | WN | Cromer Lifeboat |
| 66715 | **GB** | H | GBCM | WN | VALOUR |
| | | | | | IN MEMORY OF ALL RAILWAY EMPLOYEES |
| | | | | | WHO GAVE THEIR LIVES FOR THEIR COUNTRY |
| 66716 | **GB** | H | DFHH | FD | |
| 66717 | **GB** | H | DFHH | FD | |

### Class 66/9. New locos for Freightliner.

New low emission engines. Details awaited.

| 66951 | **FL** | H |
| 66952 | **FL** | H |

# CLASS 67     GENERAL MOTORS     Bo-Bo

**Built:** 1999–2000 by Alstom at Valencia, Spain, as sub-contractors for General Motors (General Motors model JT42 HW-HS).
**Engine:** General Motors 12N-710G3B-EC two stroke of 2385 kW (3200 h.p.) at 900 r.p.m.
**Main Alternator:** General Motors AR9/HE3/CA6B.
**Traction Motors:** General Motors D43FM.
**Maximum Tractive Effort:** 141 kN (31750 lbf).
**Continuous Tractive Effort:** 90 kN (20200 lbf) at ?? m.p.h.
**Power At Rail:** 1860 kW.
**Brake Force:** 78 t.
**Weight:** 90 t.
**Design Speed:** 125 m.p.h.
**Fuel Capacity:** 4927 litres.
**Train Supply:** Electric, index 66.
**Train Brakes:** Air.
**Dimensions:** 19.74 x 2.72 m.
**Wheel Diameter:** 965 mm.
**Maximum Speed:** 125 m.p.h.
**RA:** 8.
**Multiple Working:** AAR System.
**Notes:** All equipped with Slow Speed Control and Swinghead Automatic "Buckeye" Combination Couplers.

| | | | | | |
|---|---|---|---|---|---|
| 67001 | E | A | WAAK | CF | Night Mail |
| 67002 | E | A | WAAK | CF | Special Delivery |
| 67003 | E | A | WAAK | CF | |
| 67004 r | E | A | WAAK | CF | Post Haste |
| 67005 | E | A | WAAK | CF | Queen's Messenger |
| 67006 | E | A | WAAK | CF | |
| 67007 | E | A | WAAK | CF | |
| 67008 | E | A | WAAK | CF | |
| 67009 | E | A | WAAK | CF | |
| 67010 | E | A | WAAK | CF | Unicorn |
| 67011 | E | A | WAAK | CF | |
| 67012 | E | A | WAAK | CF | |
| 67013 | E | A | WAAK | CF | |
| 67014 | E | A | WAAK | CF | |
| 67015 | E | A | WAAK | CF | |
| 67016 | E | A | WAAK | CF | |
| 67017 | E | A | WAAK | CF | Arrow |
| 67018 | E | A | WAAK | CF | Rapid |
| 67019 | E | A | WAAK | CF | |
| 67020 | E | A | WAAK | CF | |
| 67021 | E | A | WAAK | CF | |
| 67022 | E | A | WAAK | CF | |
| 67023 | E | A | WAAK | CF | |
| 67024 | E | A | WAAK | CF | |
| 67025 | E | A | WAAK | CF | Western Star |
| 67026 | E | A | WAAK | CF | |
| 67027 | E | A | WAAK | CF | Rising Star |
| 67028 | E | A | WAAK | CF | |
| 67029 | E | A | WAAK | CF | |
| 67030 | E | A | WAAK | CF | |

# 2. ELECTRO-DIESEL & ELECTRIC LOCOMOTIVES

## CLASS 73/1    BR/ENGLISH ELECTRIC    Bo-Bo

Electro-diesel locomotives which can operate either from a DC supply or using power from a diesel engine.

**Built:** 1965–1967 by English Electric Co. at Vulcan Foundry, Newton le Willows.
**Main Generator:** English Electric 824/5D.
**Traction Motors:** English Electric 546/1B.
**Maximum Tractive Effort (Electric):** 179 kN (40000 lbf).
**Maximum Tractive Effort (Diesel):** 160 kN (36000 lbf).
**Continuous Rating (Electric):** 1060 kW (1420 h.p.) giving a tractive effort of 35 kN (7800 lbf) at 68 m.p.h.
**Continuous Tractive Effort (Diesel):** 60 kN (13600 lbf) at 11.5 m.p.h.
**Maximum Rail Power (Electric):** 2350 kW (3150 h.p.) at 42 m.p.h.
**Train Brakes:** Air, vacuum & electro-pneumatic († Air & electro-pneumatic).
**Brake Force:** 31 t.                    **Dimensions:** 16.36 x 2.64 m.
**Weight:** 77 t.                         **Wheel Diameter:** 1016 mm.
**Design Speed:** 90 m.p.h.               **Maximum Speed:** 90 m.p.h.
**Fuel Capacity:** 1409 litres.
**Train Supply:** Electric, index 66 (on electric power only).
**Multiple Working:** SR System.

Formerly numbered E 6001–20/22–26/28–49 (not in order).

**Notes:** Locomotives numbered in the 732xx series are classed as 73/2 and were originally dedicated to Gatwick Express services. 73201 and 73202 are to be retained by Gatwick Express as standby locos. These two locos, along with 73208 were available for use on service trains as this book closed for press.

| 73101 | PC | E | WNXX | HG | The Royal Alex' |
|-------|-----|------|------|------|-----------------|
| 73103 | IM | FR | SDXL | MQ | |
| 73104 | IM | FR | SDXL | CS | |
| 73105 | CE | FR | SDXL | PR | |
| 73106 | DG | E | WNXX | HG | |
| 73107 | B | FR | SDXL | PR | |
| 73108 | CE | E | WNXX | OC | |
| 73109 | ST | SW | HYSB | BM | Battle of Britain 50th Anniversary |
| 73110 | CE | E | WNXX | OC | |
| 73114 | ML | FR | SDXL | PR | |
| 73117 | IM | FR | SDXL | MQ | |
| 73118 †c | EP | EU | GPSN | OC | |
| 73128 | E | E | WNXX | HG | |
| 73129 | N | E | WNXX | HG | City of Winchester |
| 73130 †c | EP | EU | GPSN | OC | |
| 73131 | E | E | WNYX | OC | |
| 73132 | IM | E | WNZX | SP | |

| | | | | | |
|---|---|---|---|---|---|
| 73133 | **ML** | E | WPAG | HG | The Bluebell Railway |
| 73134 | **IM** | FR | SDXL | MQ | |
| 73136 | **ML** | E | WPAG | HG | Kent Youth Music |
| 73139 | **IM** | FR | SDXL | CS | |
| 73141 | **IM** | NR | QAED | LU (S) | |
| 73201 † | **GX** | P | IVGA | SL | |
| 73202 † | **GX** | P | IVGA | SL | |
| 73203 † | **GX** | GB | GBZZ | NC | |
| 73204 † | **GX** | GB | GBZZ | NC | |
| 73205 † | **GX** | GB | GBZZ | NC | |
| 73206 † | **GX** | GB | GBZZ | NC | |
| 73207 † | **GX** | GB | GBZZ | NC | |
| 73208 † | **GX** | P | IVGA | SL | |
| 73209 † | **GX** | GB | GBZZ | NC | |
| 73210 † | **GX** | P | IVGA | ZG (S) | |
| 73211 † | **GX** | P | IVGA | ZG (S) | |
| 73212 † | **RK** | NR | QAED | DF | |
| 73213 † | **RK** | NR | QAED | DF | |
| 73235 † | **GX** | P | IVGA | SL (S) | |

# CLASS 86    BR/ENGLISH    ELECTRIC    Bo-Bo

**Built:** 1965–1966 by English Electric Co. at Vulcan Foundry, Newton le Willows or by BR at Doncaster Works.
**Electric Supply System:** 25 kV AC 50 Hz overhead.

| | |
|---|---|
| **Train Brakes:** Air. | **Brake Force:** 40 t. |
| **Dimensions:** 17.83 x 2.65 m. | **Weight:** 83–86.8 t. |
| **RA:** 6. | **Multiple Working:** TDM system. |

**Train Supply:** Electric, index 74.

Formerly numbered E 3101–3200 (not in order).

**Non standard Liveries:**

86227 **AR** but with the addition of "Union Jack" bodyside vinyls.
86233 BR "Electric Blue" livery.

**Class 86/1. Class 87-type bogies & motors.**
Details as above except:
**Maximum Tractive Effort:** 258 kN (58000 lbf).
**Traction Motors:** GEC 412AZ frame mounted.
**Continuous Rating:** 3730 kW (5000 h.p.) giving a tractive effort of 95 kN (21300 lbf) at 87 m.p.h.
**Maximum Rail Power:** 5860 kW (7860 h.p.) at 50.8 m.p.h.

| | |
|---|---|
| **Weight:** 86.8 t. | **Wheel Diameter:** 1150 mm. |
| **Design Speed:** 110 m.p.h. | **Maximum Speed:** 110 m.p.h. |

| | | | | |
|---|---|---|---|---|
| 86101 | **I** | H | SAXL | LT | |
| 86102 | **I** | H | SAXL | LT | Robert A Riddles |

**Class 86/2. Standard Design rebuilt with resilient wheels and Flexicoil suspension.**

**Traction Motors:** AEI 282BZ axle hung.

**Maximum Tractive Effort:** 207 kN (46500 lbf).
**Continuous Rating:** 3010 kW (4040 h.p.) giving a tractive effort of 85 kN (19200 lbf) at 77.5 m.p.h.
**Maximum Rail Power:** 4550 kW (6100 h.p.) at 49.5 m.p.h.
**Wheel Diameter:** 1156 mm.      **Weight:** 85–86.2 t.
**Design Speed:** 125 m.p.h.      **Maximum Speed:** 100 m.p.h.

| No. | | | | | Name |
|---|---|---|---|---|---|
| 86205 | V | H | SAXL | IR | |
| 86206 | V | H | SAXL | ZH | |
| 86207 | I | H | SAXL | LT | City of Lichfield |
| 86209 | V | H | IANA | NC | City of Coventry |
| 86210 x | RX | E | WNXX | CE | C.I.T. 75th Anniversary |
| 86212 | V | H | SAXL | IR | |
| 86213 | I | H | SAXL | BH | Lancashire Witch |
| 86214 | I | H | SAXL | LT | Sans Pareil |
| 86215 | AR | H | IANA | NC | The Round Tabler |
| 86217 | AR | H | IANA | NC | City University |
| 86218 | AR | H | IANA | NC | NHS 50 |
| 86223 | AR | H | IANA | NC | Norwich Union |
| 86224 | I | H | SAXL | LT | |
| 86225 | V | H | SAXL | LT | Hardwicke |
| 86226 | V | H | SAXL | IR | |
| 86227 | AR | H | IANA | NC | Golden Jubilee |
| 86228 | I | H | SAXL | CE | Vulcan Heritage |
| 86229 | V | H | SAXL | IR | |
| 86230 | AR | H | IANA | NC | |
| 86231 | V | H | SAXL | IR | |
| 86232 | AR | H | IANA | NC | Norfolk and Norwich Festival |
| 86233 | O | H | SAXL | IR | |
| 86234 | AR | H | IANA | NC | Suffolk Relax.Refresh.Return |
| 86235 | AR | H | IANA | NC | Crown Point |
| 86237 | AR | H | IANA | NC | University of East Anglia |
| 86238 | AR | H | IANA | NC | European Community |
| 86240 | V | H | SAXL | ZH | |
| 86242 | AR | H | IANA | NC | Colchester Castle |
| 86243 x | RX | E | WNXX | CE | |
| 86245 | V | H | SAXL | IR | |
| 86246 | AR | H | IANA | NC | Royal Anglian Regiment |
| 86247 | V | H | SAXL | IR | |
| 86248 | V | H | SAXL | ZH | Sir Clwyd/County of Clwyd |
| 86249 | I | H | SAXL | PC | County of Merseyside |
| 86250 | AR | H | IANA | NC | Sheppard 100 |
| 86251 | V | H | SAXL | IR | |
| 86253 | I | H | SAXL | ZH | The Manchester Guardian |
| 86254 x | RX | E | WNXX | CE | Pebble Mill |
| 86256 | V | H | SAXL | LT | |
| 86258 | V | H | SAXL | ZH | |
| 86259 | V | H | SAXL | IR | |
| 86260 | AR | H | IANA | NC | |
| 86261 x | E | E | WNXX | CE | THE RAIL CHARTER PARTNERSHIP |

## Class 86/4. EWS-owned locomotives.

**Traction Motors:** AEI 282AZ axle hung.
**Maximum Tractive Effort:** 258 kN (58000 lbf).
**Continuous Rating:** 2680 kW (3600 h.p.) giving a tractive effort of 89 kN (20000 lbf) at 67 m.p.h.
**Maximum Rail Power:** 4400 kW (5900 h.p.) at 38 m.p.h.
**Wheel Diameter:** 1156 mm.          **Weight:** 83–83.9 t.
**Design Speed:** 100 m.p.h.          **Maximum Speed:** 100 m.p.h.
**Note:** 86426 and 86430 are on long term hire from EWS to Freightliner.

| 86401 | E | E | WNXX | CE | |
|---|---|---|---|---|---|
| 86416 x | RX | E | WNXX | TE | |
| 86417 x | RX | E | WNXX | CE | |
| 86424 | RX | E | WNXX | CE | |
| 86425 | RX | E | WNXX | CE | Saint Mungo |
| 86426 x | FL | E | DFNC | FE | |
| 86430 x | FL | E | DFNC | FE | |

## Class 86/5. Regeared locomotive operated by Freightliner.

Details as Class 86/4 except:
**Continuous Rating:** 2680 kW (3600 h.p.) giving a tractive effort of 117 kN (26300 lbf) at 67 m.p.h.
**Maximum Speed:** 75 m.p.h.          **Train Supply:** Electric, isolated.

| 86501 (86608) | FL | FL | DFGC | FE |
|---|---|---|---|---|

## Class 86/6. Freightliner-operated locomotives.

Details as Class 86/4 except:
**Maximum Speed:** 75 m.p.h.          **Train Supply:** Electric, isolated.

| 86602 | FL | FL | DFNC | FE | |
|---|---|---|---|---|---|
| 86603 | FE | FL | DHLT | SP | |
| 86604 | FL | FL | DFNC | FE | |
| 86605 | FF | FL | DFNC | FE | |
| 86606 | FF | FL | DFNC | FE | |
| 86607 | FL | FL | DFNC | FE | |
| 86609 | FL | FL | DFNC | FE | |
| 86610 | FL | FL | DFNC | FE | |
| 86611 | FF | FL | DHLT | ZC | |
| 86612 | FF | P | DFNC | FE | Elizabeth Garrett Anderson |
| 86613 | FL | P | DFNC | FE | |
| 86614 | FF | P | DFNC | FE | |
| 86615 | FL | P | DFNC | FE | Rotary International |
| 86618 | FF | P | DHLT | CE | |
| 86620 | FL | P | DFNC | FE | Philip G Walton |
| 86621 | FF | P | DFNC | FE | London School of Economics |
| 86622 | FF | P | DFNC | FE | |
| 86623 | FF | P | DHLT | CE | |
| 86627 | FL | P | DFNC | FE | |
| 86628 | FL | P | DFNC | FE | |
| 86631 | FL | P | DHLT | ZC | |
| 86632 | FL | P | DFNC | FE | |

| 86633 | FF | P | DFNC | FE | Wulfruna |
|-------|----|----|------|----|----------|
| 86634 | FL | P | DHLT | CE | |
| 86635 | FL | P | DFNC | FE | |
| 86636 | FL | P | DHLT | CE | |
| 86637 | FF | P | DFNC | FE | |
| 86638 | FF | P | DFNC | FE | |
| 86639 | FF | P | DFNC | FE | |

# CLASS 87                    BREL/GEC                    Bo-Bo

**Built:** 1973–1975 by BREL at Crewe Works.
**Electric Supply System:** 25 kV AC 50 Hz overhead.
**Traction Motors:** GEC G412AZ frame mounted.
**Maximum Tractive Effort:** 258 kN (58000 lbf).
**Continuous Rating:** 3730 kW (5000 h.p.) giving a tractive effort of 95 kN (21300 lbf) at 87 m.p.h.
**Maximum Rail Power:** 5860 kW (7860 h.p.) at 50.8 m.p.h.
**Train Brakes:** Air.                    **Brake Force:** 40 t.
**Dimensions:** 17.83 x 2.65 m.          **Weight:** 83.3 t.
**Wheel Diameter:** 1150 mm.            **Design Speed:** 110 m.p.h.
**Maximum Speed:** 110 m.p.h.          **Train Supply:** Electric, index 95.
**RA:** 6.                                **Multiple Working:** TDM system.

| 87001 | B | P | IWCA | WN | STEPHENSON |
|-------|---|---|------|----|------------|
| 87002 | P | P | IWCA | WN | |
| 87003 | V | P | IWCA | WN | Patriot |
| 87004 | V | P | IWCA | WN | Britannia |
| 87005 | V | P | SBXL | WN | |
| 87006 | V | P | IWCA | WN | George Reynolds |
| 87007 | V | P | IWCA | WN | City of Manchester |
| 87008 | V | P | IWCA | WN | City of Liverpool |
| 87009 | V | P | IWCA | WN | |
| 87010 | V | P | IWCA | WN | King Arthur |
| 87011 | V | P | IWCA | WN | City of Wolverhampton |
| 87012 | V | P | IWCA | WN | Coeur de Lion |
| 87013 | V | P | IWCA | WN | John O'Gaunt |
| 87014 | V | P | IWCA | WN | Knight of the Thistle |
| 87015 | V | P | IWCA | WN | Howard of Effingham |
| 87016 | V | P | IWCA | WN | Willesden Intercity Depot |
| 87017 | V | P | IWCA | WN | Iron Duke |
| 87018 | V | P | IWCA | WN | Lord Nelson |
| 87019 | V | P | IWCA | WN | Sir Winston Churchill |
| 87020 | V | P | IWCA | WN | North Briton |
| 87021 | V | P | IWCA | WN | Robert The Bruce |
| 87022 | V | P | IWCA | WN | Lew Adams The Black Prince |
| 87023 | V | P | IWCA | WN | Polmadie |
| 87024 | V | P | IWCA | WN | Lord of the Isles |
| 87025 | V | P | IWCA | WN | County of Cheshire |
| 87026 | V | P | IWCA | WN | Sir Richard Arkwright |
| 87027 | V | P | IWCA | WN | Wolf of Badenoch |
| 87028 | V | P | IWCA | WN | |

| 87029 | V | P | IWCA | WN | Earl Marischal |
|--------|---|---|------|----|-----------------|
| 87030 | V | P | IWCA | WN | Black Douglas |
| 87031 | V | P | IWCA | WN | Hal o' the Wynd |
| 87032 | V | P | IWCA | WN | Richard Fearn |
| 87033 | V | P | IWCA | WN | Thane of Fife |
| 87034 | V | P | IWCA | WN | William Shakespeare |
| 87035 | V | P | IWCA | WN | Robert Burns |

## CLASS 89 BRUSH Co-Co

**Built:** 1986 by BREL at Crewe Works (as sub-contractors for Brush).
**Electric Supply System:** 25 kV AC 50 Hz overhead.
**Traction Motors:** Brush. Frame mounted.
**Maximum Tractive Effort:** 205 kN (46000 lbf).
**Continuous Rating:** 4350 kW (5850 h.p.) giving a tractive effort of 105 kN (23600 lbf) at 92 m.p.h.
**Maximum Rail Power:**
**Brake Force:** 50 t.
**Weight:** 104 t.
**Design Speed:** 125 m.p.h.
**Train Supply:** Electric, index 95.
**Multiple Working:** TDM system.

**Train Brakes:** Air.
**Dimensions:** 19.80 x 2.74 m.
**Wheel Diameter:** 1150 mm.
**Maximum Speed:** 125 m.p.h.
**RA:** 6.

| 89001 | GN | SA | IECB | ZB (S) |
|-------|----|----|------|--------|

## CLASS 90 GEC Bo-Bo

**Built:** 1987–1990 by BREL at Crewe Works (as sub contractors for GEC).
**Electric Supply System:** 25 kV AC 50 Hz overhead.
**Traction Motors:** GEC G412CY frame mounted.
**Maximum Tractive Effort:** 258 kN (58000 lbf).
**Continuous Rating:** 3730 kW (5000 h.p.) giving a tractive effort of 95 kN (21300 lbf) at 87 m.p.h.
**Maximum Rail Power:** 5860 kW (7860 h.p.) at 68.3 m.p.h.
**Train Brakes:** Air.
**Brake Force:** 40 t.
**Weight:** 84.5 t.
**Design Speed:** 110 m.p.h.
**Train Supply:** Electric, index 95.
**Multiple Working:** TDM system.

**Dimensions:** 18.80 x 2.74 m.
**Wheel Diameter:** 1156 mm.
**Maximum Speed:** 110 m.p.h.
**RA:** 7.

**Non-standard liveries:**

90036 As **FE**, but has a yellow roof.

**Note:** Locomotives from Pool WEFE are loaned on a day-to-day basis to West Coast Traincare for operation by Virgin West Coast in pool IWCA.

| 90001 | b | V | P | IWCA | WN | BBC Midlands Today |
|-------|---|---|---|------|----|---------------------|
| 90002 | b | V | P | IWCA | WN | Mission: Impossible |
| 90003 | b | V | P | IWCA | WN | THE HERALD |
| 90004 | b | V | P | IWCA | WN | City of Glasgow |

| Number | | | | | Name |
|---|---|---|---|---|---|
| 90005 b | **V** | P | IWCA | WN | Financial Times |
| 90006 b | **V** | P | IWCA | WN | Modern Railways Magazine/ Roger Ford |
| 90007 b | **V** | P | IWCA | WN | Keith Harper |
| 90008 b | **V** | P | IWCA | WN | The Birmingham Royal Ballet |
| 90009 b | **V** | P | IWCA | WN | The Economist |
| 90010 b | **V** | P | IWCA | WN | 275 Railway Squadron (Volunteers) |
| 90011 b | **V** | P | IWCA | WN | West Coast Rail 250 |
| 90012 b | **V** | P | IWCA | WN | British Transport Police |
| 90013 b | **V** | P | IWCA | WN | The Law Society |
| 90014 b | **V** | P | IWCA | WN | Driver Tom Clark O.B.E |
| 90015 b | **V** | P | IWCA | WN | The International Brigades SPAIN 1936–1939 |
| 90016 b | **RX** | E | WEGE | CE | |
| 90017 b | **E** | E | WEGE | CE | |
| 90018 b | **E** | E | WEGE | CE | |
| 90019 b | **RX** | E | WEGE | CE | Penny Black |
| 90020 b | **E** | E | WEGE | CE | Sir Michael Heron |
| 90021 | **FE** | E | WEFE | CE | |
| 90022 | **FE** | E | WEFE | CE | Freightconnection |
| 90023 | **FE** | E | WEFE | CE | |
| 90024 | **GN** | E | WEFE | CE | |
| 90025 | **F** | E | WEFE | CE | |
| 90026 | **E** | E | WEFE | CE | |
| 90027 | **F** | E | WEFE | CE | Allerton T&RS Depot |
| 90028 | **E** | E | WEFE | CE | Hertfordshire Rail Tours |
| 90029 | **E** | E | WEFE | CE | The Institution of Civil Engineers |
| 90030 | **E** | E | WEFE | CE | Crewe Locomotive Works |
| 90031 | **E** | E | WEFE | CE | The Railway Children Partnership Working For Street Children Worldwide |
| 90032 | **E** | E | WEFE | CE | |
| 90033 | **FE** | E | WEFE | CE | |
| 90034 | **E** | E | WEFE | CE | |
| 90035 | **E** | E | WEFE | CE | |
| 90036 | **0** | E | WEFE | CE | |
| 90037 | **E** | E | WEFE | CE | Spirit of Dagenham |
| 90038 | **FE** | E | WEFE | CE | |
| 90039 | **F** | E | WEFE | CE | |
| 90040 | **E** | E | WEFE | CE | The Railway Mission |
| 90041 | **FL** | P | DFLC | FE | |
| 90042 | **FF** | P | DFLC | FE | Freightliner Coatbridge |
| 90043 | **FF** | P | DFLC | FE | |
| 90044 | **FF** | P | DFLC | FE | |
| 90045 | **FF** | P | DFLC | FE | |
| 90046 | **FF** | P | DFLC | FE | |
| 90047 | **FF** | P | DFLC | FE | |
| 90048 | **FF** | P | DFLC | FE | |
| 90049 | **FF** | P | DFLC | FE | |
| 90050 | **FF** | P | DFLC | FE | |

57001 "Freightliner Pioneer" passes Cholsey with a Southampton–Coatbridge Freightliner on 06/08/03.　　**Kim Fullbrook**

▲ New Virgin-liveried 57306 "JEFF TRACY" is seen at Berkswell with 82119 and the 06.40 Carlisle–Euston on 26/04/03. **Bob Sweet**

▼ New Foster Yeoman-liveried 59005 "KENNETH J PAINTER" is seen near Twyford with the 12.48 Acton–Merehead stone empties on 16/04/03. **Hugh Ballantyne**

Corus-liveried 60006 passes Milford Junction on 30/04/02 with 6V37 the 13.00 Lackenby–Llanwern steel slab train. **Jason Rogers**

▲ 66202 heads through Abercynon with 6C45 10.49 Tower–Aberthaw coal train consisting of new HTA wagons on 18/09/03. **Andrew Mist**

▼ GBRf-liveried 66711 passes Whitacre Junction on 21/06/03 with 4M21 05.42 Felixstowe–Hams Hall Intermodal. **Gavin Morrison**

▲ 67003 passes Stableford, Staffordshire with a Willesden–Glasgow Mail train on 28/05/02. **Paul Senior**

▼ Gatwick Express still use Class 73s on certain services as required. On 13/04/03 73235 passes Redhill with the 10.00 London Victoria–Gatwick Airport. **Alex Dasi-Sutton**

▲ Freightliner Green-liveried 86607 and grey 86633 head south through Ipswich station with 4M87 12.49 Ipswich yard–Trafford Park on 26/09/03. **Robert Pritchard**

▼ The Class 87s are to be progressively stored in 2004. On 26/06/03 87032 "Richard Fearn" arrives at Carlisle with the 14.30 Euston–Glasgow. **Robert Pritchard**

▲ Virgin-liveried 90007 "Lord Stamp" is seen at Norton Bridge with the 16.30 London Euston–Glasgow Central on 29/05/02. **Chris Booth**

▼ GNER-liveried 91110 is seen at York with the 09.00 Newcastle–London King's Cross service on 21/05/03. **John Chalcraft**

▲ 92031, one of only two Class 92s in EWS livery, passes Weston, near Crewe on 30/05/03 with 4S78 19.10 Daventry–Mossend Intermodal service.    **Jason Rogers**

▼ Eurotunnel shuttle loco 9004 at Cheriton with a Coquelles service on 15/03/03.
                                                                                **Shaun Bamford**

# CLASS 91          GEC          Bo-Bo

**Built:** 1988–1991 by BREL at Crewe Works (as sub contractors for GEC).
**Electric Supply System:** 25 kV AC 50 Hz overhead.
**Traction Motors:** GEC G426AZ.      **Maximum Tractive Effort:**
**Continuous Rating:** 4540 kW (6090 h.p.) giving a tractive effort of ?? kN at ?? m.p.h.
**Maximum Rail Power:** 4700 kW (6300 h.p.) at ?? m.p.h.
**Train Brakes:** Air.
**Brake Force:** 45 t.        **Dimensions:** 19.41 x 2.74 m.
**Weight:** 84 t.          **Wheel Diameter:** 1000 mm.
**Design Speed:** 140 m.p.h.      **Maximum Speed:** 125 m.p.h.
**Train Supply:** Electric, index 95.      **RA:** 7.
**Multiple Working:** TDM system.

**Note:** Locos originally numbered in the 910xx series, but renumbered upon completion of overhauls at Bombardier, Doncaster by the addition of 100 to their original number. The exception to this rule was 91023 which was renumbered 91132.

| | | | | | |
|---|---|---|---|---|---|
| 91101 | GN | H | IECA | BN | City of London |
| 91102 | GN | H | IECA | BN | Durham Cathedral |
| 91103 | GN | H | IECA | BN | County of Lincolnshire |
| 91104 | GN | H | IECA | BN | Grantham |
| 91105 | GN | H | IECA | BN | County Durham |
| 91106 | GN | H | IECA | BN | East Lothian |
| 91107 | GN | H | IECA | BN | Newark on Trent |
| 91108 | GN | H | IECA | BN | City of Leeds |
| 91109 | GN | H | IECA | BN | The Samaritans |
| 91110 | GN | H | IECA | BN | David Livingstone |
| 91111 | GN | H | IECA | BN | Terence Cuneo |
| 91112 | GN | H | IECA | BN | County of Cambridgeshire |
| 91113 | GN | H | IECA | BN | County of North Yorkshire |
| 91114 | GN | H | IECA | BN | St. Mungo Cathedral |
| 91115 | GN | H | IECA | BN | Holyrood |
| 91116 | GN | H | IECA | BN | Strathclyde |
| 91117 | GN | H | IECA | BN | Cancer Research UK |
| 91118 | GN | H | IECA | BN | Bradford Film Festival |
| 91119 | GN | H | IECA | BN | County of Tyne & Wear |
| 91120 | GN | H | IECA | BN | Royal Armouries |
| 91121 | GN | H | IECA | BN | Archbishop Thomas Cranmer |
| 91122 | GN | H | IECA | BN | Double Trigger |
| 91124 | GN | H | IECA | BN | Reverend W Awdry |
| 91125 | GN | H | IECA | BN | Berwick-upon-Tweed |
| 91126 | GN | H | IECA | BN | York Minster |
| 91127 | GN | H | IECA | BN | Edinburgh Castle |
| 91128 | GN | H | IECA | BN | Peterborough Cathedral |
| 91129 | GN | H | IECA | BN | Queen Elizabeth II |
| 91130 | GN | H | IECA | BN | City of Newcastle |
| 91131 | GN | H | IECA | BN | County of Northumberland |
| 91132 | GN | H | IECA | BN | City of Durham |

# CLASS 92        BRUSH        Co-Co

**Built:** 1993–1996 by Brush Traction at Loughborough.
**Electric Supply System:** 25 kV AC 50 HZ overhead or 750 V DC third rail.
**Traction Motors:** Brush.
**Maximum Tractive Effort:** 400 kN (90 000 lbf).
**Continuous Rating:** 5040 kW (6760 h.p.) on AC, 4000 kW (5360 h.p.) on DC.
**Maximum Rail Power:**             **Train Brakes:** Air.
**Brake Force:** 63 t.              **Dimensions:** 21.34 x 2.67 m.
**Weight:** 126 t.                 **Wheel Diameter:** 1160 mm.
**Design Speed:** 140 km/h (87 m.p.h.).    **Maximum Speed:** 140 km/h (87 m.p.h.).
**Train Supply:** Electric, index 108 (AC), 70 (DC).
**RA:** 7.

**Note:** Locomotives in pool WTWE are authorised to operate on the Eurotunnel network. These locos have had thier DC shoegear removed and only operate between Dollands Moor and Frethun.

| | | | | | |
|---|---|---|---|---|---|
| 92001 | E | E | WTWE | CE | Victor Hugo |
| 92002 | EP | E | WTAE | CE | H.G. Wells |
| 92003 | EP | E | WTAE | CE | Beethoven |
| 92004 | EP | E | WTAE | CE | Jane Austen |
| 92005 | EP | E | WTAE | CE | Mozart |
| 92006 | EP | SF | WTWE | CE | Louis Armand |
| 92007 | EP | E | WTAE | CE | Schubert |
| 92008 | EP | E | WTAE | CE | Jules Verne |
| 92009 | EP | E | WTAE | CE | Elgar |
| 92010 | EP | SF | WTWE | CE | Molière |
| 92011 | EP | E | WTAE | CE | Handel |
| 92012 | EP | E | WTWE | CE | Thomas Hardy |
| 92013 | EP | E | WTAE | CE | Puccini |
| 92014 | EP | SF | WTWE | CE | Emile Zola |
| 92015 | EP | E | WTAE | CE | D.H. Lawrence |
| 92016 | EP | E | WTAE | CE | Brahms |
| 92017 | EP | E | WTAE | CE | Shakespeare |
| 92018 | EP | SF | WTWE | CE | Stendhal |
| 92019 | EP | E | WTAE | CE | Wagner |
| 92020 | EP | EU | WNWX | CE | Milton |
| 92021 | EP | EU | WNWX | CE | Purcell |
| 92022 | EP | E | WTAE | CE | Charles Dickens |
| 92023 | EP | SF | WTWE | CE | Ravel |
| 92024 | EP | E | WTAE | CE | J.S. Bach |
| 92025 | EP | E | WTAE | CE | Oscar Wilde |
| 92026 | EP | E | WTAE | CE | Britten |
| 92027 | EP | E | WTWE | CE | George Eliot |
| 92028 | EP | SF | WTWE | CE | Saint Saëns |
| 92029 | EP | E | WTWE | CE | Dante |
| 92030 | EP | E | WTAE | CE | Ashford |
| 92031 | E | E | WTAE | CE | The Institute of Logistics and Transport |
| 92032 | EP | EU | WNWX | CE | César Franck |
| 92033 | EP | SF | WTWE | CE | Berlioz |

| 92034 | EP | E  | WTAE | CE | Kipling |
| 92035 | EP | E  | WTAE | CE | Mendelssohn |
| 92036 | EP | E  | WTAE | CE | Bertolt Brecht |
| 92037 | EP | E  | WTWE | CE | Sullivan |
| 92038 | EP | SF | WTWE | CE | Voltaire |
| 92039 | EP | E  | WTAE | CE | Johann Strauss |
| 92040 | EP | EU | WNWX | CE | Goethe |
| 92041 | EP | E  | WTAE | CE | Vaughan Williams |
| 92042 | EP | E  | WTAE | CE | Honegger |
| 92043 | EP | SF | WTWE | CE | Debussy |
| 92044 | EP | EU | WNWX | CE | Couperin |
| 92045 | EP | EU | WNWX | CE | Chaucer |
| 92046 | EP | EU | WNWX | CE | Sweelinck |

# 3. EUROTUNNEL LOCOMOTIVES

## DIESEL LOCOMOTIVES

### 0001–0005　　　　　　　MaK　　　　　　Bo-Bo

**Built:** 1992–1993 by MaK at Kiel, Germany (Model DE1004).
**Engine:** MTU 12V 396 Tc of 1180 kW (1580 h.p.) at 1800 rpm.
**Main Alternator:** BBC.　　　　　　　　　　**Traction Motors:** BBC.
**Maximum Tractive Effort:** 305 kN (68600 lbf).
**Continuous Tractive Effort:** 140 kN (31500 lbf) at 20 mph.
**Power At Rail:** 750 kW (1012 h.p.).
**Brake Force:** 120 kN.　　　　　　　　　　**Dimensions:** 16.50 x ?? x ?? m.
**Weight:** 84 t.　　　　　　　　　　　　　　**Wheel Diameter:** 1000 mm.
**Design Speed:** 120 km/h.　　　　　　　　　**Maximum Speed:** 120 km/h.
**Fuel Capacity:**　　　　　　　　　　　　　**Train Brakes:** Air.
**Train Supply:** Not equipped.　　　　　　　**Multiple Working:** Within class.

| | | | |
|---|---|---|---|
| 0001 | **GY** | ET | CO |
| 0002 | **GY** | ET | CO |
| 0003 | **GY** | ET | CO |
| 0004 | **GY** | ET | CO |
| 0005 | **GY** | ET | CO |

### 0032–0042　　　HUNSLET/SCHÖMA　　　0–4–0

**Built:** 1989–1990 by Hunslet Engine Company at Leeds as 900 mm. gauge.
**Rebuilt:** 1993-1994 by Schöma in Germany to 1435 mm. gauge.
**Engine:** Deutz of 270 kW (200 h.p.) at ???? rpm.
**Transmission:** Mechanical.　　　　　　　**Maximum Tractive Effort:**
**Cont. Tractive Effort:**　　　　　　　　　**Power At Rail:**
**Brake Force:**　　　　　　　　　　　　　　**Dimensions:**
**Weight:**　　　　　　　　　　　　　　　　**Wheel Diameter:**
**Design Speed:** 50 km/h.　　　　　　　　　**Maximum Speed:** 50 km/h.
**Fuel Capacity:**　　　　　　　　　　　　　**Train Brakes:** Air.
**Train Supply:** Not equipped.　　　　　　　**Multiple Working:** Not equipped.

| | | | | |
|---|---|---|---|---|
| 0031 | **Y** | ET | CO | FRANCES |
| 0032 | **Y** | ET | CO | ELISABETH |
| 0033 | **Y** | ET | CO | SILKE |
| 0034 | **Y** | ET | CO | AMANDA |
| 0035 | **Y** | ET | CO | MARY |
| 0036 | **Y** | ET | CO | LAWRENCE |
| 0037 | **Y** | ET | CO | LYDIE |
| 0038 | **Y** | ET | CO | JENNY |
| 0039 | **Y** | ET | CO | PACITA |
| 0040 | **Y** | ET | CO | JILL |
| 0041 | **Y** | ET | CO | KIM |
| 0042 | **Y** | ET | CO | NICOLE |

# ELECTRIC LOCOMOTIVES

## 9001–9113                    BRUSH/ABB                    Bo-Bo-Bo

**Built:** 1993–2001 by Brush Traction at Loughborough.
**Supply System:** 25 kV AC 50 Hz overhead.
**Traction Motors:** ABB 6PH.                    **Maximum Tractive Effort:** 400 kN (90 000 lbf).
**Continuous Rating:** 5760 kW (7725 h.p.) giving a TE of 310 kN at 65 km/h.
(Fleet being progressively upgraded to 7000 kW (9387 h.p.)).
**Maximum Rail Power:**                          **Multiple Working:** TDM system.
**Brake Force:** 50 t.                            **Dimensions:** 22.01 x 2.97 x 4.20 m.
**Weight:** 132 t.                                **Wheel Diameter:** 1090 mm.
**Design Speed:** 175 km/h (100 m.p.h.)          **Maximum Speed:** 160 km/h (87 m.p.h.)
**Train Supply:** Electric.                       **Train Brakes:** Air.

**CLASS 9/0. Mixed traffic locomotives.**

| | | | |
|---|---|---|---|
| 9001 | **ET** | ET | CO | LESLEY GARRETT |
| 9002 | **EB** | ET | CO | STUART BURROWS |
| 9003 | **EB** | ET | CO | BENJAMIN LUXON |
| 9004 | **EB** | ET | CO | VICTORIA DE LOS ANGELES |
| 9005 | **ET** | ET | CO | JESSYE NORMAN |
| 9006 | **EB** | ET | CO | REGINE CRESPIN |
| 9007 | **ET** | ET | CO | DAME JOAN SUTHERLAND |
| 9008 | **ET** | ET | CO | ELISABETH SODERSTROM |
| 9009 | **ET** | ET | CO | FRANÇOIS POLLET |
| 9010 | **ET** | ET | CO | JEAN-PHILIPPE COURTIS |
| 9011 | **ET** | ET | CO | JOSÉ VAN DAM |
| 9012 | **ET** | ET | CO | LUCIANO PAVAROTTI |
| 9013 | **EB** | ET | CO | MARIA CALLAS |
| 9014 | **ET** | ET | CO | LUCIA POPP |
| 9015 | **ET** | ET | CO | LÖTSCHBERG 1913 |
| 9016 | **EB** | ET | CO | WILLARD WHITE |
| 9017 | **EB** | ET | CO | JOSÉ CARRERAS |
| 9018 | **ET** | ET | CO | WILHELMENA FERNANDEZ |
| 9019 | **ET** | ET | CO | MARIA EWING |
| 9020 | **ET** | ET | CO | Nicolai Ghiaurov |
| 9021 | **ET** | ET | CO | TERESA BERGANZA |
| 9022 | **ET** | ET | CO | DAME JANET BAKER |
| 9023 | **ET** | ET | CO | DAME ELISABETH LEGGE-SCHWARZKOPF |
| 9024 | **ET** | ET | CO | GOTTHARD 1882 |
| 9025 | **EB** | ET | CO | JUNGFRAUJOCH 1912 |
| 9026 | **ET** | ET | CO | FURKATUNNEL 1982 |
| 9027 | **ET** | ET | CO | BARBARA HENDRICKS |
| 9028 | **EB** | ET | CO | DAME KIRI TE KANAWA |
| 9029 | **ET** | ET | CO | THOMAS ALLEN |
| 9031 | **ET** | ET | CO | |
| 9032 | **ET** | ET | CO | RENATA TEBALDI |
| 9033 | **ET** | ET | CO | MONTSERRAT CABALLE |
| 9034 | **ET** | ET | CO | MIRELLA FRENI |

| 9035 | **ET** | ET | CO | Nicolai Gedda |
| 9036 | **ET** | ET | CO | ALAIN FONDARY |
| 9037 | **ET** | ET | CO | GABRIEL BACQUIER |
| 9038 | **ET** | ET | CO | HILDEGARD BEHRENS |
| 9040 | **EB** | ET | CO | |

**CLASS 9/1. Freight Shuttle dedicated locomotives.**

| 9101 | **EB** | ET | CO |
| 9102 | **EB** | ET | CO |
| 9103 | **EB** | ET | CO |
| 9104 | **EB** | ET | CO |
| 9105 | **EB** | ET | CO |
| 9106 | **EB** | ET | CO |
| 9108 | **EB** | ET | CO |
| 9109 | **EB** | ET | CO |
| 9110 | **EB** | ET | CO |
| 9111 | **EB** | ET | CO |
| 9112 | **EB** | ET | CO |
| 9113 | **EB** | ET | CO |

# 9701–9707    BRUSH/BOMBARDIER    Bo-Bo-Bo

**CLASS 9/7. Increased power freight shuttle dedicated locomotives.**

**Built:** 2001–2002 by Brush Traction at Loughborough.
**Supply System:** 25 kV AC 50 Hz overhead.
**Traction Motors:** ABB 6PH.      **Maximum Tractive Effort:** 400kN (90 000lbf)
**Continuous Rating:** 7000 kW (9387 h.p.).
**Maximum Rail Power:**      **Multiple Working:** TDM system.
**Brake Force:** 50 t.      **Dimensions:** 22.01 x 2.97 x 4.20 m.
**Weight:** 132 t.      **Wheel Diameter:** 1090 mm.
**Design Speed:** 175 km/h (100 m.p.h.)    **Maximum Speed:** 160 km/h (87 m.p.h.)
**Train Supply:** Electric.      **Train Brakes:** Air.

| 9701 | **EB** | ET | CO |
| 9702 | **EB** | ET | CO |
| 9703 | **EB** | ET | CO |
| 9704 | **EB** | ET | CO |
| 9705 | **EB** | ET | CO |
| 9706 | **EB** | ET | CO |
| 9707 | **EB** | ET | CO |

# 4. CODES

## 4.1. LIVERY CODES

Livery codes are used to denote the various liveries carried. It is impossible to list every livery variation which currently exists. In particular items ignored for this publication include:

*   Minor colour variations.
*   Omission of logos.
*   All numbering, lettering and brandings.

Descriptions quoted are thus a general guide only. Logos as appropriate for each livery are normally deemed to be carried.

The colour of the lower half of the bodyside is stated first. Minor variations to these liveries are ignored.

*Code Description*

**AC**   ACTS (Netherlands) (Deep blue with a broad yellow stripe).
**AL**   Advertising livery (see class heading for details).
**AR**   Anglia Railways (turquoise blue with a white stripe).
**B**    BR blue.
**BL**   BR blue with yellow cabs, grey roof, large numbers & logo.
**BR**   BR blue with a red solebar stripe.
**CD**   Cotswold Rail (silver with blue & red logo).
**CE**   BR Engineers (yellow & grey with black cab doors & window surrounds).
**CS**   ScotRail Caledonian Sleepers (two-tone purple with silver stripe).
**CU**   Corus (silver with red logos).
**CX**   Connex (white with yellow lower body & blue solebar).
**DG**   BR Departmental (plain dark grey with black cab doors & window surrounds).
**DR**   Direct Rail Services (dark blue with light blue or dark grey roof).
**DS**   Revised Direct Rail Services (dark blue, light blue & green).
**E**    English Welsh & Scottish Railway (maroon bodyside & roof with gold band).
**EB**   New Eurotunnel (two-tone grey with a broad blue stripe).
**EN**   Enron Teesside Operations (trafalgar blue with red solebar stripe).
**EP**   European Passenger Services (two-tone grey with dark blue roof).
**ET**   Old Eurotunnel (two-tone grey & white with green & blue bands).
**F**    BR Trainload Freight (two-tone grey with black cab doors & window surrounds. Various logos).
**FB**   Revised Fragonset (freight locos) (Black with large bodyside FRAGONSET lettering).
**FE**   Railfreight Distribution International (two tone-grey with black cab doors & dark blue roof).
**FF**   Freightliner grey (two-tone grey with black cab doors & window surrounds. Freightliner logo).
**FG**   First Group corporate Inter-City livery (indigo blue with a white roof & gold, pink & white stripes).
**FL**   Freightliner (dark green with yellow cabs).
**FO**   BR Railfreight (grey bodysides, yellow cabs & large BR double arrow).

| **FP** | Old First Great Western (green & ivory with thin green & broad gold stripes). |
| **FR** | Fragonset Railways (black with silver roof & a red bodyside band lined out in white). |
| **FX** | Felixstowe Dock Company. |
| **FY** | New Foster Yeoman (blue/silver. Cast numberplates). |
| **G** | BR Green (plain green, with white stripe on main line locomotives). |
| **GB** | GB Railfreight (blue with orange cantrail & solebar stripes, orange cabs). |
| **GG** | BR green (two-tone green). |
| **GIF** | GIF (Spain) light blue with dark blue band. |
| **GL** | First Great Western Classes 47 & 57 (green with a gold stripe). |
| **GN** | Great North Eastern Railway (dark blue with a red stripe). |
| **GS** | Royal Scotsman/Great Scottish & Western Railway (maroon). |
| **GW** | Great Western Railway (green, lined out in black & orange. Cast numberplates). |
| **GX** | Gatwick Express InterCity (dark grey/white/burgundy/white). |
| **GY** | Eurotunnel (grey & yellow). |
| **HA** | Hanson Quarry Products (dark blue & silver). |
| **HN** | Harry Needle Railroad Company (orange/grey, lined out in black). |
| **I** | BR InterCity (dark grey/white/red/white). |
| **IM** | BR InterCity Mainline (dark grey/white/red/light grey & yellow lower cabsides except shunters). |
| **IR** | Ian Riley Engineering (grey with green band). |
| **K** | Black. |
| **LH** | BR Loadhaul (black with orange cabsides). |
| **LW** | LNWR black with grey & red lining. |
| **MA** | Maintrain (Light blue). |
| **ML** | BR Mainline Freight (Aircraft blue with silver stripe). |
| **MM** | Old Midland Mainline (Teal green with grey lower body sides & three tangerine stripes). |
| **MN** | New Midland Mainline (Thin tangerine stripe on the lower bodyside, ocean blue, grey & white). |
| **MR** | Mendip Rail (Green, red & silver). |
| **N** | BR Network South East (white & blue with red lower bodyside stripe, grey solebar & cab ends). |
| **O** | Non standard livery (see class heading for details). |
| **P** | Porterbrook Leasing Company (purple & grey). |
| **PC** | Pullman Car Company (umber & cream with gold lettering). |
| **RG** | BR Parcels (dark grey & red). |
| **RK** | Railtrack (green & blue). |
| **RL** | RMS Locotech (blue & red). |
| **RP** | Royal Train (claret, lined out in red & black). |
| **RR** | Regional Railways (dark blue/grey with light blue & white stripes, three narrow dark blue stripes at cab ends). |
| **RT** | RT Rail (black, lined out in red). |
| **RV** | Riviera Trains (Oxford blue). |
| **RX** | Rail Express Systems (dark grey & red with or without blue markings). |
| **SB** | Serco Railtest blue (deep blue with white Serco brandings). |
| **SL** | Silverlink (indigo blue with white stripe, green lower body & yellow doors). |
| **ST** | Stagecoach/South West Trains (white & blue with orange & red stripes). |
| **V** | Virgin Trains (red with black doors extending into bodysides, three white lower bodysides stripes). |

| | |
|---|---|
| **VP** | Virgin Trains shunters (black with a large black & white chequered flag on the bodyside). |
| **VT** | New Virgin Trains (silver with red roof. Red swept down at ends). |
| **WA** | Wabtec Rail (black). |
| **WN** | West Anglia Great Northern Railway (white with blue, grey & orange stripes). |
| **Y** | Plain yellow. |
| **YO** | Foster Yeoman (blue/silver/blue. Cast numberplates). |

# 4.2. OWNER CODES

Locomotives and rolling stock are owned by various companies and private owners and are allotted codes as follows:

*Code    Owner*

| | |
|---|---|
| 11 | 33111 Preservation Group |
| 40 | The Class 40 Preservation Group |
| 50 | The Fifty Fund |
| 71 | 71A Locomotives |
| 90 | Deltic 9000 Locomotives |
| A | Angel Trains |
| AM | Alstom |
| BT | Bombardier Transportation |
| CD | Cotswold Rail Engineering |
| CM | Cambrian Trains |
| CN | The Carriage and Traction Company |
| DP | The Deltic Preservation Society |
| DR | Direct Rail Services |
| DT | The Diesel Traction Group |
| E | English Welsh & Scottish Railway |
| EN | Enron Teesside Operations |
| ET | Eurotunnel plc. |
| EU | Eurostar (UK) |
| FG | First Great Western |
| FL | Freightliner |
| FR | Fragonset Railways |
| FX | The Felixstowe Dock & Railway Company |
| FY | Foster Yeoman |
| H | HSBC Rail (UK) |
| HA | The Hanson Group |
| HJ | Howard Johnston Engineering |
| HN | Harry Needle Railroad Company |
| HS | Harry Schneider |
| IR | Ian Riley Engineering |
| JK | Dr. John Kennedy |
| MA | Maintrain |
| NR | Network Rail |
| P | Porterbrook Leasing Company |
| RL | RMS Locotech |
| RT | RT Rail Tours |
| RV | Riviera Trains |

| SA | Sea Containers Railway Services |
| SC | South Central |
| SF | SNCF (Société Nationale des Chemins de fer Français) |
| SO | Serco Railtest |
| SW | South West Trains |
| VW | Virgin West Coast |
| WA | Wabtec Rail |
| WB | Wales & Borders |
| WC | West Coast Railway Company |
| WF | Western Falcon Rail (Alan and Tracy Lear) |
| WN | West Anglia Great Northern Railway |
| X | Sold for scrap/further use and awaiting collection or owner unknown |

# 4.3. LOCOMOTIVE POOL CODES

Locomotives are split into operational groups ("pools") for diagramming and maintenance purposes. The official codes used to denote these pools are shown in this publication.

| Code | Pool |
| --- | --- |
| ATLO | Virgin West Coast locomotives (Alstom controlled). |
| CDJD | Serco Railtest Class 08. |
| CREL | Cotswold Rail Engineering operational locomotives – contract hire. |
| CRHH | Cotswold Rail Engineering operational locomotives – spot-hire contracts. |
| CROL | Cotswold Rail Engineering stored locomotives. |
| CRUR | Cotswold Rail Engineering stored locomotives – undergoing restoration. |
| DFFT | Freightliner Class 47 with "Dock Mode" for the Felixstowe branch. |
| DFGC | Freightliner Class 86/5. |
| DFGM | Freightliner Class 66/5, Intermodal traffic. |
| DFHH | Freightliner Heavy Haul Classes 66/5 and 66/6. |
| DFLC | Freightliner Class 90. |
| DFLH | Freightliner Heavy Haul Class 47. |
| DFLM | Freightliner Class 47 with multiple working equipment. |
| DFLS | Freightliner Class 08. |
| DFNC | Freightliner Class 86/6. |
| DFRT | Freightliner Class 66/5 & 66/6. Network Rail contracts and general traffic. |
| DFTZ | Freightliner Class 57. |
| DHLT | Freightliner. Locomotives awaiting maintenance/repair/disposal. |
| DNLL | Deltic 9000 Locomotives Limited locomotives. |
| GBCM | GB Railfreight Class 66. Railfreight contracts. |
| GBRT | GB Railfreight Class 66. Netwrork Rail contracts. |
| GBZZ | GB Rail. Stored pool. |
| GPSN | Eurostar (UK) Class 73. |
| GPSS | Eurostar (UK) Class 08. |
| GPSV | Eurostar (UK) Class 37. |
| HBSH | Wabtec hire shunting locomotives. |
| HGSS | Maintrain Class 08 (Tyseley) |
| HISE | Maintrain Class 08 (Derby). |

| | |
|---|---|
| HISL | Maintrain Class 08 (Neville Hill). |
| HJSE | First Great Western Class 08 (Landore). |
| HJSL | First Great Western Class 08 (Laira). |
| HJXX | First Great Western Class 08 (Old Oak HST & St. Philips Marsh). |
| HLSV | Wales & Borders Class 08. Hire locomotive. |
| HNRL | Harry Needle Railroad Company hire locomotives. |
| HNRS | Harry Needle Railroad Company stored locomotives. |
| HQXX | West Anglia Great Northern Railway Class 03. |
| HWSU | South Central Class 09. |
| HYSB | South West Trains Standby locomotive. |
| IANA | Anglia Railways Classes 47 & 86. |
| ICCP | Virgin West Coast Class 43. |
| IECA | Great North Eastern Railway Class 91. |
| IECB | Great North Eastern Railway Class 89. |
| IECP | Great North Eastern Railway Class 43. |
| IMLP | Midland Mainline Class 43 (for use on London St. Pancras–Nottingham and Sheffield/Leeds services). |
| IMRL | Midland Mainline Class 43 (for use on "Project Rio" London St. Pancras–Manchester services). |
| IVGA | Gatwick Express Class 73. |
| IWCA | Virgin West Coast Classes 87 & 90. |
| IWLA | First Great Western Classes 47 & 57. |
| IWRP | First Great Western. Class 43. |
| KCSI | Bombardier Class 08 (Ilford). |
| KDSD | Bombardier Class 08 (Doncaster). |
| KESE | Alstom Class 08 (Eastleigh). |
| KGSS | Bombardier Class 08 (Glasgow). |
| KWSW | Bombardier Class 08 (Wolverton). |
| MBDL | Non TOC owned diesel locomotives. |
| MOLO | RT Rail Tours (Michael Owen). |
| QADD | Network Rail Class 31. |
| QAED | Network Rail Class 73. |
| QCAR | Network Rail. New Measurement Train Class 43. Fitted with front end recording equipment. |
| RFSH | Wabtec hire fleet. |
| RTLO | Riviera Trains. Operational Fleet. |
| SAXL | HSBC Rail (UK). Off lease. |
| SBXL | Porterbrook Leasing. Off lease locomotives. |
| SDFR | Fragonset Railways. Operational locomotives. |
| SDMS | Fragonset Railways. Museum locomotives. |
| SDXL | Fragonset Railways. Stored locomotives. |
| WAAK | EWS Class 67. |
| WBAH | EWS Class 66. Anglia & Southern. |
| WBAI | EWS Class 66. North Eastern (South). |
| WBAK | EWS Class 66. Great Western. |
| WBAM | EWS Class 66. Scotland, non-RETB fitted. |
| WBAN | EWS Class 66. Midland. |
| WBAT | EWS Class 66. North Eastern (North). |
| WBBM | EWS Class 66. Scotland, RETB fitted. |
| WCAI | EWS Class 60. North Eastern (South). |
| WCAK | EWS Class 60. Great Western. |

| | |
|---|---|
| WCAN | EWS Class 60. Midland. |
| WCAT | EWS Class 60. North Eastern (North). |
| WDAG | EWS Class 59/2. |
| WEFE | EWS Class 90. |
| WEGE | EWS Class 90. On hire to Anglia Railways. (Locomotives in pool WEFE may substitute). |
| WFGA | EWS Class 58. For hire contract to the Netherlands. |
| WFGF | EWS Class 58. Locomotives for possible future foreign hire contracts. |
| WGAI | EWS Class 56. North Eastern (South). |
| WGAT | EWS Class 56. North Eastern (North). |
| WKGF | EWS Class 37. Locomotives for possible future foreign hire contracts. |
| WHCD | EWS Class 47/7. Dual braked. |
| WHDD | EWS Class 47. Dual braked. |
| WHRD | EWS Class 47. Special Trains. |
| WHTN | EWS Class 47. Hired to Serco Railtest. |
| WKAC | EWS Class 37. Anglia & Southern. |
| WKAD | EWS Class 37. Midlands & North West. |
| WKBM | EWS Class 37. Scotland. |
| WKCK | EWS Class 37. Hired to Wales & Borders. |
| WKGS | EWS Class 37. On hire to Spain. |
| WKSN | EWS Class 37. Network Rail Sandite contract. |
| WMOC | EWS. Heritage locomotives. |
| WNSO | EWS. Main line locomotives – sold awaiting collection. |
| WNSS | EWS. Main line locomotives – stored serviceable. |
| WNTR | EWS. Main line locomotives – tactical reserve. |
| WNXX | EWS. Main line locomotives – stored unserviceable. |
| WNYX | EWS. Main line locomotives – authorised for component recovery. |
| WNZX | EWS. Main line locomotives/Shunting locomotives – awaiting disposal. |
| WPAG | EWS Class 73. |
| WSAS | EWS Shunting locomotives (Anglia & Southern Zone). |
| WSAW | EWS Shunting locomotives (on hire to Allied Steel & Wire). |
| WSGW | EWS Shunting locomotives (Great Western Zone). |
| WSMD | EWS Shunting locomotives (Midlands Zone). |
| WSNE | EWS Shunting locomotives (North East England). |
| WSNW | EWS Shunting locomotives (North West England). |
| WSSC | EWS Shunting locomotives (Scotland). |
| WSWX | EWS Shunting locomotives – Locos for repair. |
| WSXX | EWS Shunting locomotives – Stored. |
| WSYX | EWS Shunting locomotives – component recovery only. |
| WTAE | EWS Class 92. Dollands Moor–Wembley–Mossend–Doncaster & Crewe–Trafford Park Routes. |
| WTWE | EWS. Class 92 Eurotunnel only. |
| XHCK | Direct Rail Services. Operational locomotives (Classes 37, 47 & 66). |
| XHSD | Direct Rail Services. Operational locomotives (Classes 20 & 33). |
| XHSS | Direct Rail Services. Stored locomotives. |
| XYPA | Mendip Rail. Class 59/1. |
| XYPO | Mendip Rail. Class 59/0. |

# 4.4. ALLOCATION & LOCATION CODES

Allocation codes are used in this publication to denote the normal maintenance base of each operational locomotive. Howver, maintenance may be carried out at other locations and may also be carried out by mobile maintenance teams.

Location codes are used to denote common storage locations whilst the full place name is used for other locations. The designation (S) denotes stored. However, when a loco pool code denotes that a loco is stored anyway, then the (S) is not shown.

| Code | Location | Depot Operator |
|------|----------|----------------|
| AN | Allerton (Liverpool) | EWS |
| AY | Ayr | EWS |
| BA | Basford Hall Yard (Crewe) | *Storage location only* |
| BG* | Billingham | Enron Teesside Operations |
| BH | Barrow Hill (Chesterfield) | Barrow Hill Engine Shed Society |
| BI | Brighton | South Central |
| BM | Bournemouth | South West Trains |
| BN | Bounds Green (London) | GNER |
| BR* | MoD Bicester DSDC | Ministry of Defence |
| BQ | Bury (Greater Manchester) | East Lancashire Railway |
| BS | Bescot (Walsall) | EWS |
| BZ | St. Blazey (Par) | EWS |
| CD | Crewe Diesel | EWS |
| CE | Crewe International Electric | EWS |
| CF | Cardiff Canton | Wales & Borders/EWS |
| CP | Crewe Carriage | London & North Western Railway |
| CQ | Crewe (The Railway Age) | Carriage & Traction Company |
| CO | Coquelles (France) | Eurotunnel |
| CS | Carnforth | West Coast Railway Company |
| CW* | Crewe South Yard | *Storage location only* |
| CZ | Central Rivers T&RSMD (Burton) | Bombardier Transportation |
| DF | Derby RTC | Fragonset Railways |
| DR | Doncaster TMD | EWS |
| DY | Derby Etches Park | Maintrain |
| EC | Edinburgh Craigentinny | GNER |
| EH | Eastleigh | EWS |
| ES* | On hire to Spain | GIF |
| FB | Ferrybridge | EWS |
| FD | Freightliner diesels (general code) | Freightliner |
| FE | Freightliner electrics (general code) | Freightliner |
| FX* | Felixstowe | Felixstowe Dock & Railway Company |
| HE | Hornsey (London) | West Anglia Great Northern |
| HG | Hither Green (London) | EWS |
| HM | Healey Mills (Wakefield) | EWS |
| IM | Immingham | EWS |
| IP | Ipswich | EWS |
| IR* | Immingham Railfreight Terminal | *Storage location only* |
| IS | Inverness | ScotRail |

| KM | Carlisle Kingmoor | Direct Rail Services |
|----|-------------------|---------------------|
| KR | Kidderminster | Severn Valley Railway |
| KT | MoD Kineton (Warwickshire) | Ministry of Defence |
| KY | Knottingley | EWS |
| LA | Laira (Plymouth) | First Great Western |
| LB | Loughborough | Brush Traction |
| LD | Leeds Midland Road | LNWR/Freightliner |
| LE | Landore (Swansea) | First Great Western |
| LL | Edge Hill (Liverpool) | West Coast Traincare |
| LO | Longsight Diesel (Manchester) | First North Western |
| LR | Leicester | EWS |
| LT | MoD Longtown (Cumbria) | Ministry of Defence |
| LU* | MoD Ludgershall | Ministry of Defence |
| MD | Merehead | Mendip Rail |
| MG | Margam (Port Talbot) | EWS |
| ML | Motherwell (Glasgow) | EWS |
| MM | Fire Service College, Moreton-in-Marsh | Cotswold Rail |
| MQ* | Meldon Quarry (Okehampton) | *Storage location only* |
| MS* | Mountsorrel (Barrow-upon-Soar) | Lafarge |
| NC | Norwich Crown Point | Anglia Railways |
| NL | Neville Hill (Leeds) | Arriva Trains  NorthernMaintrain |
| NP | North Pole International (London) | Eurostar (UK) |
| OC | Old Oak Common locomotive (London) | EWS |
| PC* | Polmadie (Glasgow) | West Coast Traincare |
| PM | St. Philips Marsh (Bristol) | First Great Western |
| PR* | Peak Rail (Darley Dale) | Peak Rail |
| QU* | Quidhampton (Salisbury) | Imerys |
| RL | Ropley (Hampshire) | Mid Hants Railway |
| SI | Soho (Birmingham) | Maintrain |
| SL | Stewarts Lane (London) | Gatwick Express/VSOE |
| SP | Springs Branch CRDC (Wigan) | EWS |
| SR | Temple Mills (Stratford, London) | EWS |
| SY | Saltley (Birmingham) | EWS |
| SU | Selhurst (Croydon) | South Central |
| SZ | Southampton Maritime | Freightliner |
| TB | Tilburg (Netherlands) | NedTrain |
| TE | Thornaby (Middlesbrough) | EWS |
| TM | Tyseley Locomotive Works | Birmingham Railway Mueseum |
| TO | Toton (Nottinghamshire) | EWS |
| TS | Tyseley (Birmingham) | Maintrain |
| TT* | Toton Training School Compound (Notts) | *Storage location only* |
| TY | Tyne Yard (Newcastle) | EWS |
| WN | Willesden (London) | West Coast Traincare |
| ZA | RTC Business Park (Derby) | Serco/AEA Technology |
| ZB | Doncaster Works | Wabtec |
| ZC | Crewe Works | Bombardier Transportation |
| ZD | Derby Litchurch Lane Works | Bombardier Transportation |
| ZF | Doncaster Works | Bombardier Transportation |
| ZG | Eastleigh Works | Alstom |
| ZH | Springburn Works Glasgow | Alstom |

| ZI | Ilford Works | Bombardier Transportation |
| ZK | Kilmarnock Works | Hunslet Barclay |
| ZN | Wolverton Works | Alstom |
| ZP | Horbury Works (Wakefield) | Bombardier Transportation |

*= unofficial code.

## 4.5. ABBREVIATIONS

| CRDC | Component Recovery & Disposal Centre. |
| DSDC | Defence Storage & Distribution Centre |